Puffin Books

THE JUNGLE SALE

> Once, before I went to school,
> When I was only four,
> I went to the village Jungle Sale
> With Mary from next door.

This is a collection of poems set in a child's world of joined-up writing, class projects, spelling tests and playtime; events that will be recognized and enjoyed by children of all ages. There's also a crocodile tramping down to the local swimming pool, a kite stuck up a tree, a rabbit who digs like a dog and a trip to the beach.

A funny and observant collection of poems by a teacher who knows just what primary school life is like. June Crebbin lives in Birstall, Leicester.

THE
JUNGLE SALE

Poems by
JUNE CREBBIN

Illustrated by Thelma Lambert

PUFFIN BOOKS

For John

PUFFIN BOOKS

Published by the Penguin Group
Penguin Books Ltd, 27 Wrights Lane, London W8 5TZ, England
Penguin Books USA Inc., 375 Hudson Street, New York, New York 10014, USA
Penguin Books Australia Ltd, Ringwood, Victoria, Australia
Penguin Books Canada Ltd, 10 Alcorn Avenue, Toronto, Ontario, Canada M4V 3B2
Penguin Books (NZ) Ltd, 182–190 Wairau Road, Auckland 10, New Zealand

Penguin Books Ltd, Registered Offices: Harmondsworth, Middlesex, England

First published by Viking Kestrel 1988
Published in Puffin Books 1990
10 9 8 7 6 5 4 3 2

Text copyright © June Crebbin, 1988
Illustrations copyright © Thelma Lambert, 1988
All rights reserved

Printed in England by Clays Ltd, St Ives plc

CONTENTS

The Jungle Sale

Once, before I went to school,
When I was only four,
I went to the village Jungle Sale
With Mary from next door.

The hall was full of people,
But, as far as I could see,
No sign of a lion or tiger,
Not a single chimpanzee.

And where were the man-eating spiders?
Gorillas? Cockatoos?
Mary said that she'd buy me
A present – but what could I choose?

There were piles of clothes on the tables
That stood around the hall,
But no sign at all of an elephant
On the white elephant stall.

Still, I did go home with a monkey
With wrap-around arms and tail,
And whatever Mum says, I've kept him –
He's definitely Not for Sale.

First and Last

I like to be first in the playground,
I like to stand by the tree,
I like to imagine that all this space
Belongs entirely to me.

I walk from the tree to the waste-bin,
I walk across to the hedge,
I zig-zag across to the bushes
And then I go right round the edge.

When my friends arrive in the playground,
That's when the real games begin.
But I'm not a very fast runner
So I don't often try to join in.

Sometimes they say, "Are you playing?"
As I practise bouncing my ball,
But they always ask too many people.
I'd rather stay by the wall.

And when I hear the whistle
At precisely five to nine,
And everyone rushes and pushes,
I choose to be last in the line.

I like to be last in the playground,
I take a last look around, and then,
I promise myself that tomorrow
I'll be first in the playground again.

Kite

I'm
part of a
project on flight.
I'm supposed to attain
a great height. But
unfortunately
I got stuck
in a tree
so
it
looks
like
I'm
here
for
the
night!

Best Day

"This is the best day of my life,"
said Jimmy to the school secretary.

"Oh, yes," she said. "Why's that?"
"I'm being sent home," he said.
"Oh, dear," she said. "Why's that?"

"Spots," he said. "All over."

And he showed her.

Cobweb Morning

On a Monday morning
We do spellings and Maths.
And silent reading.

But on the Monday
After the frost
We went straight outside.

Cobwebs hung in the cold air,
Everywhere.
All around the playground,
They clothed the trees,
Dressed every bush
In veils of fine white lace.

Each web,
A wheel of patient spinning.
Each spider,
Hidden,
Waiting.

Inside,
We worked all morning
To capture the outside.

Now
In our patterns and poems
We remember
The cobweb morning.

Break-up

I've always sat next to Shirley,
And what I'd like to know
Is why's she been moved to another desk?
Why did she have to go?

It's true we sometimes argued,
And when we can't agree
It's true I've pinched her once or twice,
But the teacher didn't see.

I know we shouldn't borrow,
But I do it all the time,
And when I use her crayons and things,
Shirley doesn't mind.

I don't like this girl I'm next to,
The one in Shirley's place,
She keeps her crayons and rubbers
Zipped up in a pencil case –

And she's started this nasty rumour –
I'd like to see it proved –
I don't believe it, but *she* said
Shirley *asked* to be moved.

Why don't you . . .?

Why don't you join the choir?

Well, you have to sing on your own, don't you?

Don't be silly.
A choir means everyone singing together –
A chorus of voices.
Sometimes we sing hymns or carols,
Sometimes we sing songs – with ACTIONS!
We're in all the school concerts,
We sing to old people,
We take part in competitions,
We go all over – even to the cathedral.
We have a really good time.
You'd enjoy it.

O.K. How do I join?

First, you have to sing on your own –

Harmony

Upright I stand, though on you I depend.
Silent, I wait for the silence to end.
One lock have I, but more than one key.
Open me up – you'll be able to see
Hammers of wood set out in a row,
Strings right behind them, ready to go.
So, pull up a stool, don't hang around,
Together we'll make a note-worthy sound!

A piano

The Gerbil's Funeral

The gerbil's going bald, Miss,
The gerbil's lost its hair,
Its neck and face and ears, Miss
Are practically bare!

Oooh, Miss, what if she dies?
What if, after all,
She's suffering from the plague, Miss?
We could have a funeral!

Who'll bring the coffin?
"I," said Robin.
"I've got a box that I'm not usin'.
I'll bring the coffin."

Who'll dig the grave?
"I," said Dave,
"With my Dad's spade,
I'll dig the grave."

Who'll sing a dirge?
"I," said Jim,
"I can sing a solemn hymn.
I'll sing a dirge."

Who'll be chief mourner?
"I," said Lorna.
"I'm the one who brought her.
I'll be chief mourner."

Who'll make the cross?
"I," said Claire.
"I'll carve it with care.
I'll make the cross."

Who'll bring the flowers?
"I," said Rose.
        and Daisy
            and Heather . . .

What about me?
What about me?
What about me?

All the boys and the girls
Fell to fighting and to shouting –

WHO'LL BE THE PREACHER?
"I," said the teacher,
"I'll be the preacher,
If the need arises.
Meanwhile, we'll hope for the best.
Life's full of surprises.
Now, what about this spelling test?"

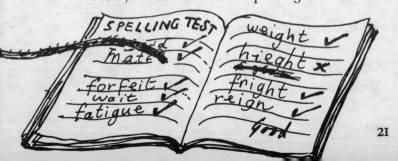

Joined Writing

I am learning to do
Joined Writing.

I have written pages
of sand and land and band.
I have written thousands
of book, look, took and cook.

I can now write
enormous, multiplication and kangaroo
without taking my pencil off the paper . . .

By now most people have been given a pen.

I have thirty-three ticks,
seventeen "Good Efforts",
one "Good"
and a "What happened to you today?"

When I get "Excellent",
I will get a pen.

Pocket

In my pocket were –

Two broken biscuits
Three torn tissues
Four cracking conkers
Five smooth stones
Six sticky sweets
Seven stamps for swops
Eight copper coins
Nine coloured crayons
Ten matching marbles

and

one

HUGE

hole!

The Robin

I tried to write a poem today,
I tried to make it rhyme,
I tried to get the meaning right
But every single time
I thought I'd got the hang of it,
I thought I'd got it right,
I found I couldn't think of a word
To rhyme with bird
Or, that is, robin.

I didn't want to say,
I saw a robin.
It was bobbing
Along and sobbing.
Because it wasn't.

So I started again.

Once, last winter, in the snow,
I was out in the garden
At the bird table,
When I turned round
And saw, on the path beside me,
A robin.

It was so close
I could have touched it.
It took my breath away.

I have never forgotten
The red of it
And the white snow falling.

On a Monday Morning

– a sing-along song

What shall we do with a naughty schoolboy?
What shall we do with a naughty schoolboy?
What shall we do with a naughty schoolboy
On a Monday morning?

Throw him in the bin with the mouldy rubbish,
Throw him in the bin with the mouldy rubbish,
Throw him in the bin with the mouldy rubbish
On a Monday morning.

Oh, dear, the smell's disgusting!
Oh, dear, the smell's disgusting!
Oh, dear, the smell's disgusting
On a Monday morning!

What shall we do with a naughty schoolgirl?
What shall we do with a naughty schoolgirl?
What shall we do with a naughty schoolgirl
On a Monday morning?

Hang her from the ceiling and tickle her
tootsies,
Hang her from the ceiling and tickle her
tootsies,
Hang her from the ceiling and tickle her
tootsies
On a Monday morning.

Oh, dear, the smell's disgusting!
Oh, dear, the smell's disgusting!
Oh, dear, the smell's disgusting
On a Monday morning!

What shall we do with an angry teacher?
What shall we do with an angry teacher?
What shall we do with an angry teacher
On a Monday morning?

Lock her in the cupboard with a hungry tiger,
Lock her in the cupboard with a hungry tiger,
Lock her in the cupboard with a hungry tiger
On a Monday morning.

Oh, dear, the smell's disgusting!
Open up the door, the smell's disgusting!
Here comes the tiger – and the tiger's smiling!
On a Monday morning.

One of Those Days

Kevin's ripped his paper,
Kelly's lost her pen,
And Tim is having trouble
With his nine times ten.

Mary isn't sure
Where her ruler's gone,
And Sally-Ann is certain
All her sums are wrong.

Matthew can't remember
What the teacher said,
His face and page are white
But his eyes are red.

Gemma thinks her writing's
Getting far too small,
If there's any further shrinking
There'll be none at all.

Christopher, by accident,
Bumped into Jane,
And the smudge has spoilt her picture
And she wants to start again –

Oh, the floods are flowing freely,
There's a lot of rain about,
Thank goodness when it's playtime
And the sun comes out!

29

If Only

I'm waiting to see the headmaster
And my legs are beginning to ache.
I've been standing here ever since lunch time,
How long is he going to take?

He said, "Wait there till I'm ready,"
And his meaning was perfectly clear,
I've been standing here over an hour.
He could have forgotten I'm here.

I wish I'd never played football.
I wish I wasn't at school.
"Rules are made to be kept," he says,
And I do. Well, I do, as a rule.

But today, I just couldn't help it
And I would have scored a goal,
Only the ball went too high and it vanished,
So I went through the hedge, through the hole.

I knew by the crash where I'd find it,
I knew by the pieces of glass.
It looked like the whole of the greenhouse
Was scattered about on the grass.

I offered to pay for the damage,
I offered to sweep up the mess,
But the lady who lived there ignored me
And asked for my name and address.

HEADMASTER
D. WALLIS-JONES

She wouldn't listen to reason,
She wouldn't listen at all.
She telephoned the headmaster
And confiscated my ball.

I'd rather be doing my lessons
Than standing here on my own.
I know he's still in there, because
I heard him answer the 'phone.

I wish I could turn back the clock,
I wish I could go back in time.
People keep passing, and staring
As though I'd committed a crime.

I didn't do it on purpose.
If only he'd let me explain,
I'd give him my Scout's word of honour
That I'd try not to do it again.

They'll be painting by now in the classroom.
He's wasted my whole afternoon.
I wish it was over and done with –
Surely he'll talk to me soon.

Nothing

What
to it!   did
Nothing   you
Miss.   say,

easy,   Kevin?

It's   Nothing,

nothing.   Miss.

say   Oh

can   really?

you   That's

how   clever.
to know   like   I'd

One Day

When the story's boring,
I skip pages.
I've been doing it
For ages.
One day,
I'd really like
To read like Mike.
He never leaves
Anything out.
And he knows
What the story's about.

Practising

I want to give up the violin
because
I don't like it,
I don't like the teacher
and I hate practising . . .

I want to give up the violin
because
I don't like it,
the teacher doesn't like me
and I hate practising . . .

I want to give up the violin
because
I don't enjoy it,
I have tried it for three years,
Practising is a waste of time . . .

I want to give up the violin
because
I don't enjoy it,
I *have* tried it for three years,
Practising takes up a *lot* of time
and my school work is suffering . . .

Right. Now, where's my Dad?

Tea-time

What's for tea today?

　What do you fancy?

Oh, bed and butter,
Ham and leg,
Knees on toast
And trampled egg,
Chocolate lake
And leaf stew,
Smashed potato:
That'll do!

　Fancy!

Or oodles and oodles
Of plop suey and poodles . . .

　Well, it's fish and chips.
　How's that for starters?

Great! What's for afters?

　Apple pie and mustard!

Rest Assured

No head have I nor any feet,
No mouth have I with which to eat,
Yet I can stand while you may sit,
So, rest assured, depend on it –
Though many qualities I lack,
Four legs have I and a very strong back.

A chair

37

```
        C               D A     L
        L           A N           S
        O           S
        G                           R   S
        S                         E
                B               I
                O           A
    W           O       R
    E           T     A
        L L I E S                       S I N S
                P               A
                L           C
S L I P P     L         O
        E   I M
        R   S
            O
            L
            L
            S


    A   S H O E - T R E E
```

CLOGS · SANDALS · BOOTS · WELLIES · TRAINERS · MOCCASINS · SLIPPERS · PLIMSOLLS

A SHOE-TREE

Spring Has Arrived!

Tulips are shouting from borders:
Blossom froths on the tree:
Bluebells swing in the flower beds.

Old men are sitting in doorways:
Children run in the park:
Shoppers stroll in the sunshine.

Grass is growing like crazy:
Trees take over the sky –
Today, as if by magic,

Spring has arrived!

Beware!

The crocodile is coming!
It's heading for the pool,
It's swaying down the road
From the local Primary School.
Better keep your distance,
Better close your doors –
Beware the fearful clamour
From its ever-open jaws!
Be careful not to stumble
As you hurry from the street:
Remember that the crocodile
Has sixty tramping feet!
Through the city jungle
The creature marches on.
Wisely, shoppers stand aside
And wait until he's gone.
It's going to cross the busy street –
It starts to leave the path –
Attacked by snarling traffic
It's completely cut in half –
The head continues on its way,
The tail, delayed, just laughs
And runs to catch it up
At the Municipal Baths.
The crocodile is swimming
In the Public Swimming Pool,
But soon it will be heading
For the local Primary School.
So, better keep your distance,
Better if you try
To find a place to hide
While the crocodile goes by!

My Rabbit

When my rabbit
is out in his run,

he digs up the ground
like a dog,

washes himself
like a squirrel,

sits on his back legs
like a kangaroo,

leaps and twirls
like an acrobat,

but

when he eats a cabbage leaf,
as is his daily habit,
he delicately nibbles it
EXACTLY like a rabbit!

Giant Moth

One windy day,
when I was taking a message
across to the Infant School
with my friend,

I saw
a giant moth
land
on the school field.

It was so big
I could see clearly
its yellow and brown markings.

As it rested
I saw
each wing lift
and tremble
before it rose in the air again.

My friend said
it was only a big leaf,

But I said,
I think I know a Giant Moth
when I see one.

Choosing Time

Shall I
finish my picture,
tidy my drawer,
wash up the paint-pots,
sweep up the floor?

Time's ticking by,
not a moment to lose,
why do I never
know what to choose?

I'd copy my friend
but, need I say more?
she's having trouble,
she's not too sure

whether to
finish her picture,
tidy her drawer . . .

Get Well Soon

Dear Mrs Appleby,
I hope you get well soon.

I was away
While you were away.
I only just got back today.

We've had five different teachers.
Well, I've had three —
You see,
I was away
Yesterday
And the day before.

We've done Chinese kites,
"Flags of the World",
"A Day in the Life of a Squirrel"
And now this letter.

I still have a cough.
I might be off
Tomorrow.

Here is a joke:
"What is green and deadly and flies?
A budgie with a pea-shooter."

I hope you're feeling better.
Yours sincerely, JOHN.

P.S. Will you be away long?

Spelling Rules, OK?

Each Monday we're given ten spellings
To learn by the end of the week,
And some are easy like "lovely",
And some are hard like "unique".

There's a lot of rules to remember,
Like when to change y into i
As in jellies and wellies and berries,
And when you want more than one fly . . .

You change f into v to make half into halves,
There's a piece of pie in piece,
There's i before e except after c
As in thief and in chief and in niece . . .

To make stare into staring, you knock off the e,
There's a silent k in knot,
To make skip into skipping, you double the p –
It's hard to remember the lot.

But by the end of the week, I'm word-perfect,
And then, what I really detest
Is when the teacher is busy
And *forgets* the spelling test!

And if, on the following Monday,
I manage to get them all right,
My teacher then says, "But the real test
Is how well you spell when you write!"

skip
skipping

berry
berries

Summer-time

summer-time
is when the teacher
releases the dam
in the playground
and we pour on to the field;

summer-time
is when playtime seems to last for ever
and when the bell does go

we
   t
     r
       i
         c
           k
             l
               e
                     back
                        across
                           the
                               playground
                                    into
                                        school.

Best Stroke

My best stroke is my breast stroke,
I'm not much good at crawl,
And when I try to butterfly
I can't do that at all.

I'm sure I couldn't duck-dive
Or paddle like a dog,
But maybe that's because
I'm a breast-stroke-swimming frog!

Ups and Downs

Teachers like you
to
sit up
shut up
and put your hand up
when you have something to say.

Teachers like you
to
calm down
sit down
and put your pencil down
when you've only just picked it up.

Teachers like you
to
speak up
make your mind up
and stand up straight
when they're talking to you.

Teachers like you
to
settle down
put your ruler down
and keep your voice down
when it's supposed to be choosing time.

Teachers,
like you,
have good days
and bad days!

Non-swimmer

I can't swim.
No one knows
At this school yet.
I'm not letting on
To anyone.
I'll just forget my kit.

I've done it before.

When the teacher says:
"Who is a swimmer?"
I keep still.
And when he says:
"Who is a non-swimmer?"
I keep very still.
And no one notices.

I've done it before.

When I get home,
My mother says:
"When's your swimming day, then?"
And I say: "Thursday."
I don't mean to.
I just forget.

One thing's for sure.
Mum'll remember my swimming kit.

She's done it before.

The Boat Bus

The bus sails through the rain:
From the top deck, I can see
The greedy river flowing
Where green fields used to be.

Rain batters the windows,
Streams across the glass,
Trees, with a stutter of gun-fire,
Attack us, as we pass.

We sway from village to village,
Up many a hill and down,
Trying to keep a look-out
For the lights of the distant town.

The bus stops in the High Street:
We step on to land again,
Where pavements shine in the street light
And only puddles remain.

Dinner-time Rhyme

Can you tell me, if you please,
Who it is likes mushy peas?
    Louise likes peas.
How about Sam?
    Sam likes Spam.
How about Vince?
    Vince likes mince.
How about Kelly?
    Kelly likes jelly.
How about Trish?
    Trish likes fish.
How about Pips?
    Pips likes chips.
How about Pete?
    Pete likes meat.
How about Sue?
    Sue likes stew.
How about Greg?
    Greg likes egg.
How about Pam?
    Pam likes lamb.

OK, then, tell me, if you can –
How about Katerina Wilhelmina Theodora
Dobson?

    She goes home for dinner . . .

Silk-moth Monitor

In our classroom
we have thirty-three children,
one teacher
and fifty-two Chinese silk-moths.

I am the Chinese silk-moth monitor.

Each day
I have to check the oak leaves
and decide whether to replace them,
so that the Chinese silk-moths,
which are at the second stage
of their development –
that is to say, caterpillars –
can enjoy a healthy diet.

Each day
I have to record their progress,
so I have put a spot
on the one I call Leroy,
a typical specimen, and –
each day –
I measure him.
This can take some time.
He is a fast mover.

Friday is cleaning-out day.
This is when I give
every caterpillar
the chance to exercise properly.
Crawling along my finger
provides the challenge
of a different environment.

I could have been
the dinner-register monitor,
but I prefer working with animals.

In the Park

                                                slide

                                        the

                                of

                        top

                the

            to

        up

    way

long

    a

    It's

b
u
t
f
u
n
w
h
i
z
z
i
n
g
d
o
w
n
o
ntheotherside.

Hot Afternoon

Under the overgrown bramble,
my cat noses through the weeds,
turns and turns,
following her tail
and settles.

Above her, leaves form a canopy.

She seems to sleep.

Under the overgrown bramble,
my cat wakes instantly
at the sound of food
on a plate.

Pleas-e!

Bumble bee, bumble bee,
Fly away home;
Leave my naked toes
Alone!

Bumble bee, bumble bee,
Don't you know
Another place where
You can go?

Bumble bee, bumble bee,
When I doze off,
I don't need you, so
Buzz off!

Sticks

In colours of the rainbow or in white,
With a helping hand, I can draw and write.
Though I have no voice and cannot speak,
I have been known to snap and squeak.
Each time I'm used, there's less of me.
I fall to pieces easily.
Though commonplace, this you should know,
From rock I come, to dust I go.

Chalk

Holiday

How many more are we going to see?
One castle is very much
Like another, you know, and
I feel as though I've seen enough . . .
Dad, why don't you and Mum go round this one?
Anyway, someone's got to get the lunch ready.
You go ahead. I'll fetch the fish and chips!

My Grannies

I hate it, in the holiday,
When Grandma brings her pets to stay –
Her goat, her pig, her seven rats
Scare our dog and chase our cats.
Her budgies bite, her parrots shout –
And guess who has to clean them out?

My other Gran, the one I like,
Always brings her motor-bike,
And when she takes me for a ride
To picnic in the countryside,
We zoom up hills and whizz round bends –
I hate it when her visit ends!

To the Beach

every
day
on
h
o
l
i
d
a
y
I
g
o

down
t
h
e
steps
e
x
c
i
t
e
d
l
y

jump   waves

                  swim   the

             and   in   sea

to   the

Smile, Please!

Can I borrow your comb?
Can I borrow your brush?
The photographer's arrived
And it's rush, rush, rush.

Rush to look in the mirror,
Rush to get in the queue,
Don't forget to smile,
That's the thing to do.

"What a load of miseries!
What a dreary lot!
What about a smile, then?
Is that the best you've got?

Sit on the edge of the box, dear,
Turn your head to me,
What did you say your name was?
Can you count to three?"

How I hate it when
I hear the dreaded click,
I'm sure I wasn't smiling,
I sat there feeling sick.

And when the photos come
And the teacher gives them out,
I just do not want to look
Till there's no one else about.

I clutch it to my chest
So that only I can see.
Well, I know my Gran'll like it:
She'll say it's just like me.

"Can I look at yours?
You can look at mine."
"No, it's awful." "No, it's not."
"Yours is lovely." "Yours is fine."

True friends always say
They like the one of you.
I agree with them – and smile,
It's the only thing to do!

"And Then"

My teacher says
I mustn't say
"And then",
Like when I write,
"I went into the forest
And then I saw a huge bear
And then the huge bear
Lumbered towards me
And then I grabbed him
By the throat
And then . . ."

My teacher says
Every now
And then
I should stop.

But I don't know when.

And if I did
I might not get started again

And then
I'd never finish the story.

School

Sometimes, in the middle of term, when I
Come to school, I look forward to the
Holidays, when I can go swimming,
Or play tennis, or generally mess around,
Only I know I always run out of things I
Like doing after the first few days.

Open/Close/Open/Close

I am one, yet sound like two,
I will gladly work for you
On paper, cloth or even hair,
If you handle me with care.
An instrument, though never played,
Two handles and a double blade,
Closed, I cannot help you, so
Open me up and I'm ready to go!

A pair of scissors

Race Against Time

And here we are now,
Ready for the start,
Pencils poised,
Breathing heavily,
Eyes on the starter . . .

And they're off!
Four fives, two fives, three fives,
Eight fives –
Eight fives? Eight fives?
FORTY!
And they're
Over that one
And on to the next –
And coming up now
To the half-minute mark.
Half a minute,
Half a minute to go
And one of them is trailing –
No, no,
He's still there
He's still in the race –
Nine fives, nine fives?
Nine fives?
FORTY-FIVE!
And into the straight,
Down the paper,
And they're
Coming up to the finish
With five seconds to go,
Four, three, two –
And they've finished!
With a second to spare
And they're
Breathing freely now,
Papers over,
Pencils down.

The School Carol

Deck the classrooms now with holly,
Christmas time has just begun.
Here's a reason to be jolly,
No more lessons, lots more fun!
Christmas cards and Christmas pictures
Are the order of the day;
Let us paint a red-nosed reindeer
Pulling Santa on his sleigh.

Deck the classrooms now with streamers,
Thread some snow of cotton-wool,
Spray a snow scene on the windows,
Make some crackers we can pull.
Decorate the tree with tinsel
Green and silver, red and gold,
Sew a needle-case for Grandma,
Soon the secrets can be told.

Deck the hall with sprays of holly,
Dress up in your party gear.
Here's a reason to be jolly,
No more lessons till next year!
Hurry to the Christmas Disco,
Come along and join the fun –
Dance and swing, and sing together:
Happy Christmas, everyone!

A Hard-to-crack Case

If suits go in a suit-case,
Pencils in a pencil-case,
Books go in a book-case,
Do police go in a police case?

If tea goes in a tea-bag,
Shopping in a shopping-bag,
Pegs go in a peg-bag,
Does a school go in a school-bag?

If a horse goes in a horse-box,
Money in a money-box,
Toys go in a toy-box,
Are there windows in a window-box?

If eggs go in an egg-cup,
Coffee in a coffee-cup,
Fruit goes in a fruit-cup,
Is there butter in a buttercup?

If flowers go in a flower-pot,
Honey in a honey-pot,
Stew goes in a stew-pot,
Does fuss go in a fuss-pot?

All these questions needing answers
Make a hard-to-crack case.
The only answer I can find is
I'm a little nut-case!

Cheerio, I'm off!

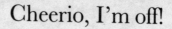

I'm off now then.

What?
Pardon?

It's in my pocket.
I won't lose it.

I have got a hanky.
The dinner money's in it –
I won't *use* it.

I'm off now then.

What?
Pardon?

I have fed the rabbit.
He doesn't need water.

I'll clean him out tonight;
I'll clean him out
After football.

I'm off now.

What?
Pardon?

I have cleaned them
With polish –

No, the hanky's in my pocket
With the dinner money.

I *won't* lose it.

Cheerio, I'm off!

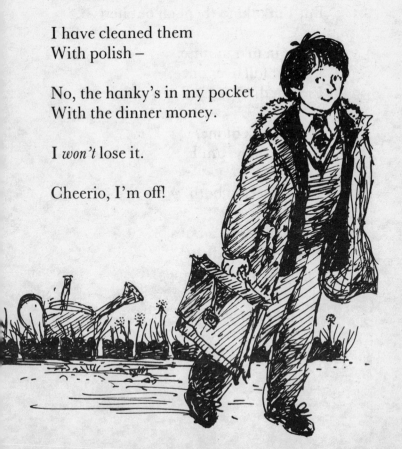

Hello, I'm Home!

I'm not dirty –

My track suit's not dirty either
Because I took it off,
Even though it was cold.

I'm taking off my boots now.
They're dirty, of course,
But I'm taking them off out here.

I'll be in in a minute.
I didn't fall over once.
I'm not dirty –

Look. Look at me,
I'm not dirty, am I?

I don't need a bath.

Why do I need a bath
When I'm not dirty?
I played a clean game.

I'm going, I'm going –

BUT I'M NOT DIRTY . . .

Racing
A Beginner's
Guide

Racing
A Beginner's Guide

Third Edition

JOHN CAIG

AND

TIM DAVISON

fernhurst
BOOKS

BICENTENNIAL
1807
WILEY
2007
BICENTENNIAL

John Wiley & Sons, Ltd

Third edition © Fernhurst Books 2007
First published 1988 by Fernhurst Books, Duke's Path, High St, Arundel, BN18 9AJ, UK

Copyright © 2007 John Wiley & Sons Ltd
Published under the Fernhurst imprint by John Wiley & Sons Ltd, The Atrium, Southern Gate, Chichester, West Sussex PO19 8SQ, England
Telephone (+44) 1243 779777

Email (for orders and customer service enquiries): cs-books@wiley.co.uk
Visit our Home Page on www.wiley.com

Other Wiley Editorial Offices

John Wiley & Sons Inc., 111 River Street, Hoboken, NJ 07030, USA
Jossey-Bass, 989 Market Street, San Francisco, CA 94103-1741, USA
Wiley-VCH Verlag GmbH, Boschstr. 12, D-69469 Weinheim, Germany
John Wiley & Sons Australia Ltd, 42 McDougall Street, Milton, Queensland 4064, Australia
John Wiley & Sons (Asia) Pte Ltd, 2 Clementi Loop #02-01, Jin Xing Distripark, Singapore 129809
John Wiley & Sons Canada Ltd, 22 Worcester Road, Etobicoke, Ontario, Canada M9W 1L1

Wiley also publishes its books in a variety of electronic formats. Some content that appears in print may not be available in electronic books.

Anniversary logo Design: Richard J. Pacifico

Library of Congress Cataloguing in Publication Data
Caig, John.
  Racing : a beginner's guide : correct for the 2005-2008 racing rules of sailing / John Caig & Tim Davison. -- 3rd ed.
      p. cm.
  ISBN 978-0-470-51262-3
  1. Sailboat racing. I. Davison, Tim. II. Title.
  GV826.5.C27 2007
  797.1'4--dc22
                        2006103538

British Library Cataloguing in Publication Data
A catalogue record for this book is available from the British Library

ISBN-13: 978-0-470-51262-3 (PB)

Typeset in 9/12 Swiss 721 by Laserwords Private Limited, Chennai, India
Printed in Italy by PrinterTrento, Trento
This book is printed on acid-free paper responsibly manufactured from sustainable forestry
in which at least two trees are planted for each one used for paper production.

Contents

CONTENTS

Acknowledgements

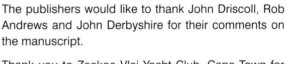

The publishers would like to thank John Driscoll, Rob Andrews and John Derbyshire for their comments on the manuscript.

Thank you to Zeekoe Vlei Yacht Club, Cape Town for providing the facilities for this shoot. Especial thanks to the 29er and 420 sailors and Davey James & Doug Alison for their time.

All photographs taken by Liz Mansell

Introduction

This book is intended as a guide for people who have already learned to sail and would like to go a step further and start racing.

Many people catch the 'bug' after their first race, and it remains with them for the rest of their lives. Why is this? There are those who are naturally competitive and always want to test their skill against others. Some people are less competitive but enjoy racing because it offers the best opportunity to get the best out of their boats. There is nothing like a few races to show you just how well or badly you are sailing!

You will probably be itching to enter a race before you have read to the end of this book, so we have laid out the first four chapters to give you enough knowledge to take part in a race with some degree of confidence. The remainder of the book is designed to help you improve your performance, and a glossary of terms used in racing is included at the end.

Many successful skippers start their racing careers by crewing with more experienced helms. It can be an advantage to get the feel for racing before you start out on your own, but it's by no means essential. You may learn faster by finding your own way, and this book will help you do just that.

We hope you enjoy your racing as much as we have done, and continue to do. It will give you an absorbing hobby for life. Good sailing!

John Caig and Tim Davison

Choosing a Boat

If you don't already have a boat you may be wondering what to buy. If you have been crewing for someone then you will already know a little about what you might want. But if you are starting from scratch you have two options: either join a club first (which limits your choice of boat) or buy a boat first (which limits your choice of club).

It's probably best to visit your nearest club and consider the suitability of the boats they sail. If you have a family and intend to race with them you need a boat large enough to take them. Otherwise, one of the singlehanders may well be best for you. Also, take physical factors into account. If you are not particularly heavy then you would be wise to consider a boat with a small sail area that will not be too strenuous. For example, if you buy a standard Laser and you weigh only 54 kg (120 lbs) you will begin to be at a disadvantage when the wind reaches 15 knots. In a 420 you could be in with the champions in any weather.

Another consideration is, of course, cost. You have to be able to afford to buy your boat, but you also need to be aware of the cost of maintaining it, including buying new sails when it becomes necessary (at least every other season, if you want to stay competitive).

It's often advisable to go for a used boat at first, buying a new one only when you have learned enough to know how you want it to be fitted out. Don't be afraid to buy and sell boats: why stick in a class you aren't enjoying or in a boat that's holding you back?

There's a huge variety of boats out there: one of them is sure to be right for you.

What is a Race?

Most dinghy races are sailed round a number of marker buoys specified by the Sailing or Race Committee, and called 'The Course'.

You have to round each buoy in a specified direction. 'Buoy X to port' for example means you round it anticlockwise, leaving it on the port side of your boat. Similarly, 'all marks to starboard' means you round all buoys clockwise. You will often see a shorthand form such as 1S, 2P, etc.; this means leave buoy 1 to port, buoy 2 to starboard, and so on. Sometimes the buoys are shown on a coloured background, red indicating a buoy to be left to port, green meaning leave it to starboard.

THE COURSE

This is always laid down in the sailing instructions, which are posted on a notice board or handed out as a printed sheet.

Sailing instructions are always given in writing and the rules prevent their being given orally. It is important that competitors study these instructions before the race.

There are several types of course depending on the local geography, but many are triangular in shape and are intended to test all points of sailing. The start is across an imaginary line between two points (often a

Rounding a mark to port.

committee boat and buoy) and is usually signalled by the lowering of a flag and the sounding of a horn or gun.

All boats must be behind this line when the starting signal is made. A warning signal (usually five minutes before the start) and preparatory signal (with four minutes to go) allow competitors to start their watches and do their own countdown.

If there is any discrepancy, the time is taken from the preparatory signal.

Sometimes a distance mark is laid to keep competitors clear of the committee boat: you are not allowed to sail between this mark and the committee boat. Note that this mark is not necessarily *on* the startline; in fact it is usually over the line.

The first leg is usually upwind to the first mark, and most boats will make a number of tacks to reach it. This should have the effect of spreading out the fleet so there is not too much congestion at the first mark.

Rounding a mark to starboard.

Subsequent legs are 'off the wind', and made up of reaches or runs, eventually ending back near the starting area. The course is often repeated, the number of rounds being specified in the sailing instructions.

If the wind drops, the race can be shortened by a shortened course signal that is usually code flag S – a blue rectangle on a white background. The race then ends at the next mark after the signal was made. Finishes are usually into the wind and entail crossing a finishing line between two marks or a committee boat and mark.

The Triangle/Sausage course

This was originally used as the Olympic course, and is in our view one of the fairest, with all points of sailing included. The start is upwind for the reasons already mentioned. The second and third legs are reaches; sometimes one is a close reach and the other a broad reach. At the leeward mark the course turns upwind once more. A run follows the second rounding of the weather mark. This sequence of legs is repeated until

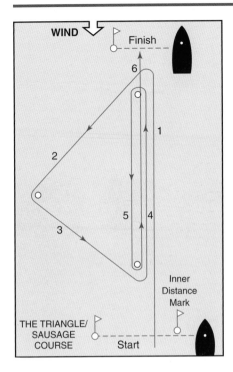

THE TRIANGLE/ SAUSAGE COURSE

the finish, which is either between the weather mark and a committee boat or at a finish line upwind of the weather mark.

Where space does not permit such a course – for instance on a small inland reservoir – then the course should be set to give the best balance of beating, reaching and running.

For asymmetric boats a windward – leeward course is often used, because the run provides lots of opportunities for tactics.

HANDICAP RACING

When boats of different types are going to race together a handicap race is organised. There are two main types of handicap race.

Conventional handicap races

All boats start on the same signal, as in a single-class race, but the Race Officer records their finishing times. When all the boats have finished, their times are multiplied by a handicap correction figure to provide the final race results. This correction is arrived at by considering the results of many club races over many years. It cannot be completely fair, particularly in the case of boats that perform very differently in differing conditions (such as catamarans), but nevertheless it can be a basis for quite satisfactory inter-class racing.

Pursuit races

In pursuit racing, the starting time of each boat is determined by its handicap number. The slowest set off first, and the race is run for a predetermined length of time. The finish line is not laid until the finish time is due, and the first across the line wins. In order to make the final results as fair as possible for slower boats that are trailing, a number of finish lines could be laid simultaneously. In fact, the fairest results would be determined by an aerial photograph – not all that practical for your average club race!

Basic Racing Rules

You may feel that you need to know all the rules before you take part in your first race, but if you waited until you knew them all you would never get started – there are quite a number of rules and some need a lot of experience to interpret.

A few basic rules are all you need to begin with and many club sailors never get around to learning more (although of course they are always intending to!). When you want to know more read *The Rules in Practice* by Bryan Willis, also published by Fernhurst Books.

THE NEED FOR RACING RULES

No sport or game can be successful without rules of some sort, and yacht racing is no exception. What's more, unlike football and cricket, there are normally no referees or umpires, so observance of the rules relies on the obedience and honesty of the competitors. When there is a disagreement the only option is a *protest*, which is heard by an independent body of knowledgeable yachtsmen called a Protest Committee. Non-sailing people often misunderstand the word protest, but those involved with the sport soon come to realise that it is the only fair method of sorting out who is in the right in a particular rules incident. The International Sailing Federation (ISAF) Rules are used throughout the world in local, international and Olympic competition. Although some variations can be made to suit local club conditions, the basic rules remain the same wherever you race. So what are they?

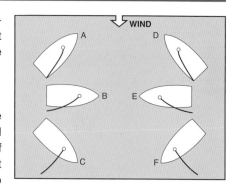

Port gives way to starboard

You are on starboard tack when the boom is on the port side and the wind is coming from your starboard side. A boat sailing on starboard tack has the right of way and, unless there is danger of a collision, must hold a steady course when a port tack boat is near (so as not to mislead her). Most boats will start the race on starboard tack because it is important to have right of way in the congested area of the startline. In the diagram, D, E and F have right of way over A, B and C who have to keep clear.

The overtaking boat must keep clear

When you are approaching another boat from behind you must be sure that you keep clear. In the diagram, G is overtaking and is not allowed to sail into the back of H. This situation is very likely to occur at the start when the boats nearest to the startline slow up and those just behind tend to run them down.

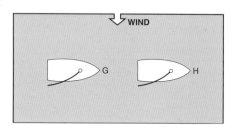

The overtaking boat 533 must keep clear of 530

A windward boat shall keep clear of a leeward boat

The windward boat is the one that is nearer to the wind than the other – that is, it is upwind of the other. The rule says that it has to keep clear of the downwind boat. This rule is one of natural justice. Since a boat being

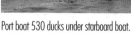
Port boat 530 ducks under starboard boat.

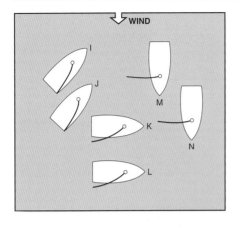

The windward boat (right) must keep clear.

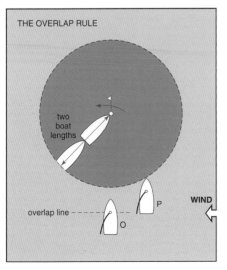

overtaken to windward will have its wind taken away, it is only fair that it should be given the right to defend its position. The leeward boat (the one furthest from the wind) may turn up towards the wind (or *luff*) and the windward boat has to keep clear.

This rule is of particular importance at the start when the boats are close together, and on the reach when everyone is fighting for clear wind. In the diagram, I must keep clear of J, K must keep clear of L, and N must keep clear of M.

A boat must give room at a mark to another boat overlapping it on the inside

This means that as two or more boats are about to round a mark the one on the outside must give room to the one on the inside – if the inside boat can establish an overlap, in proper time, on the boat outside her. Proper time is judged by drawing an imaginary circle around the buoy with a radius of two boat lengths. The inside boat needs to establish its overlap before the outside one enters this circle. The inside crew often shout 'Water!' to establish their rights, though this is not essential according to the rules. In the diagram, O has the right to round inside P.

Touching a mark

If you touch a mark, sail well clear. Immediately make one turn, including a tack and a gybe, keeping clear of all other boats. Then sail on.

ALTERNATIVE PENALTIES

Occasionally you may infringe a racing rule particularly when you are new to racing. In most cases the sailing instructions will allow you to make a 'Two Turn Penalty' i.e. make two turns in the same direction including two tacks and two gybes as soon as you are clear of the incident. Should you hit a mark you are only required to carry out a 'One Turn Penalty'.

PROTESTS

You should bear in mind that every time a collision occurs between two boats, one or both will have infringed a rule. If you consider that you are in the right and the other competitor doesn't do their turns you should inform them that you are going to protest by hailing 'Protest'. (If your boat is more than six metres long you also have to display a red flag with a swallow-tail cut out of it.) After the race fill out a protest form. It is best to seek advice from someone experienced who can make sure that you quote the appropriate rule and indeed check that you are probably in the right!

Remember it is not unsporting to protest. Since there is no referee watching your race the rules need to be implemented afterwards. Without protests anarchy would reign!

Armed with an understanding of the rules above, you are ready to take part in your first race.

GOLDEN RULES

- Port gives way to starboard.

- The overtaking boat keeps clear.

- The windward boat keeps clear of the leeward boat.

- At a mark, the outside boat gives room to the inside boat (provided the overlap was established in proper time).

Your First Race

Don't forget that, beginner or not, you will be a very welcome addition to the fleet. Those who usually do well, the 'hot shots', will be only too pleased to come home having beaten a larger fleet. Those nearer the back of the fleet will welcome the chance to beat someone! Don't be disappointed if you are last – just give it a go! Do remember that, particularly in the heat of the start, some competitors can get a bit excited and may shout at you if they think you are infringing the rules. Don't let this worry you; they may not have had time to realise you are a beginner and you'll probably find that back in the clubhouse they are quite decent. But do speak to them about any such incident afterwards, particularly if you are unsure of which rule you may have infringed. It's a good chance to learn as well as make friends.

Now, how should you approach the race? First you must read the sailing instructions or at the very least speak to a friend and establish the essential information (it's not a good idea to expect to follow everyone else). The course referred to in this chapter will be a triangular one with the sequence beat-reach-reach-beat-run-beat, often called the triangle/sausage course. In practice you are likely to encounter more complicated courses at your local club. Nevertheless, the triangle/

sausage described covers all the relevant points of sailing. (A diagram of this course is given on page 5).

To begin with you need to know the startline. This will be an imaginary line between two points and is often limited in length by extra marker buoys. Typically, the startline is defined as a line between the mast on a committee boat and a buoy, with a limit mark near the committee boat. This inner distance limit mark is not necessarily on the line, but boats must not pass between it and the committee boat. The committee boat may be replaced by an onshore mast or pole, which may be portable or permanent.

Next you need to know the course: the order in which the buoys are to be rounded and on which side they are to be passed. If a mark is to be left to port then you are required to pass around it on its right-hand side (anti-clockwise) leaving the buoy on your left. If you have any doubt where to go, make yourself a course card, put it in a clear plastic bag and tape it to the boat.

You also need to know the number of laps to be sailed and where the finish is. During the race you must watch the committee boat: if code flag S is flown it means the course is being shortened—perhaps because the wind is falling light.

Finally you must know the time of the start. Do try to get on the water in plenty of time: this is the most common failing of beginner and expert alike. Time always seems to go faster than you expect and arriving at the start without sorting out your strategy can be a costly mistake.

THE START

You can expect the start to be upwind (to windward), so plan to start on starboard tack about one third of the way down the line from the starboard end. (Later we will discuss how to choose the favoured end but, for the moment, assuming a line of 60 metres (200 feet) or less, the first-timer should do as suggested.)

Try a few practice runs, timing yourself to get an idea how far you travel in, say, 60 seconds. If the wind is light try to keep close to the line in case it drops further, leaving you stranded. This is of particular importance if there is any current taking you away from the line.

Watch out for the warning signal. This will be a sound signal accompanied by your class flag and is usually five minutes before the start. Start your stopwatch on this signal and check it at the preparatory signal four minutes before the start. Remember that the racing rules come into force after this second signal so keep a good look out (as you should at all times).

From your previous trial runs you will have established how far you can expect to travel in one minute. Try to be somewhere near this one-minute distance from the line at about one and a half minutes before the start. This will allow you to slow your approach as you get closer to the line. The easiest way to slow up is to ease the sails until they are half flapping, sheeting them in again when more speed is needed.

Heading closer to the wind without sheeting in will also slow you up. Be careful not to drop down on other boats to leeward or you may be greeted by shouts of 'Up up!' indicating that you must luff to avoid a collision. Try to approach the line with space below you, so you can free off (ease sails and steer away from the wind) at the last minute and cross the line with maximum speed. In any event, if the helmsman keeps an eye on the boat to leeward it will help him judge his own start. In the meantime the crew should look to weather and warn the helmsman if the weather boat is about to sail over the top of them. You will hear a further sound signal one minute before the start, and a signal at the start – that makes four signals in all: 5, 4, 1 Go.

THE FIRST BEAT

Once the gun has gone and you have crossed the line you will be beating towards the first mark. Don't be discouraged by the fact that the boats around you are going faster or closer to the wind. Most novices tend not to pull the mainsail in close enough. As you gain experience you will find that sail trim is quite critical in getting the best speed out of your boat. The important

533 has opted to pass astern of the starboard tack boat rather than risk infringing the rule (and losing a friend...)

thing at this stage is to keep steering closer to the wind until the sails begin to flap (luff) and the boat begins to slow, and then bearing away until full speed is achieved once more. The ability to spot the moment just before

This perfectly-timed tack by No 4 (on port) enables her to put a lee-bow on No 3

the boat begins to slow is important in your development of good upwind speed. You will soon learn to luff continually and bear away *subtly* so you can respond to the continuous changes in the wind's direction. Don't follow boats that are only half a dozen boat lengths ahead of you; they will slow you up because they interfere with your wind. Tack away to get clear air. On the other hand don't go way off on your own; there is probably a very good reason why the majority of the racing fleet is going the other way!

From time to time you may encounter other boats on the opposite tack. If you are on starboard you have the right of way and *must* hold your course. Call 'Starboard' if you think the crew of the other boat haven't seen you. Even on starboard you should keep a good lookout. In the event of substantial damage you will still carry some responsibility for not keeping clear even though you had the right of way! If you are on port tack you must keep clear of a boat on starboard either by tacking or bearing away under her stern. If you aren't confident of staying ahead after a tack you would do best to pass under her stern. (If you tack and she then sails over you, you will be slowed unnecessarily.)

Remember that when you need to bear away to duck someone's stern you must ease the mainsheet. If you don't, the weather helm will make bearing off much more difficult, particularly if it is windy, and you risk a collision. Ease sails as you bear away and trim them in

giving her a tactical advantage (see Chapter 7, page 44, for more on lee-bowing).

When rounding the weather mark let the mainsheet out progressively.

again quickly as you luff up: this way you will lose very little distance – in fact you will momentarily be able to point higher just after crossing behind the other boat, due to her effect on the wind direction (see diagram opposite).

Try to approach the windward mark on starboard tack if other boats are likely to arrive at the same time: a port tack approach is risky.

THE REACH

Once around the windward mark you will be on a reach. Ease out the sheets until the sails are just about to flap. Pull the centreboard up to about halfway and head directly towards the next mark unless there is a very good reason to do otherwise. Concentrate on maximum speed by careful trimming of the sails. If you

PASSING ASTERN — WIND — sail on

bear away

luff: wind lifts behind the starboard boat

Let it out too fast and you dunk the crew.

begin to overtake another boat you must be prepared for her to luff you – that is, steer up into the wind to stop you overtaking. To avoid this happening, keep well clear of boats to leeward. If there is a collision you will probably be in the wrong.

If another boat does luff you away from the direct course, it's probably best to ease your sheets, slow up, and bear off under her stern.

The next buoy is the gybe mark. Should you be overlapped on the inside you must give plenty of room for that boat to round inside you. Gybe firmly with the centreboard half up, and make sure that at the moment the boom comes across you straighten up to prevent the boat spinning up into the wind. Once on the new reach, head straight for the next mark: you will lose out if you sail a curved path to windward of the rhumb line.

Rounding the leeward mark differs from the previous one in that you will need the centreboard right down just before going round. Steer a little wide as you approach it, sheeting in the sails as you tighten up round the mark.

Now you are on the beat once more. This time the boats will be spaced out a little and you will probably be further behind. Don't worry, just concentrate on sailing as fast as possible.

Without following close behind anyone in particular, follow the general direction of the leaders; they are probably doing the right thing.

Try not to overstand the windward mark – if you go past the layline (see diagram) you will need to reach down to the buoy, wasting valuable distance (X on the diagram).

THE RUN

After rounding the windward mark for the second time, the next leg is a run downwind to the leeward mark. Raise the centreboard approximately three-quarters of the way up, and ease the sheets out all the way. The direct line to the leeward mark will usually be quickest, unless you are flying a spinnaker (or sailing a catamaran).

If it is at all windy, however, you must be careful not to gybe accidentally. The best way to avoid this is to sail a little higher than the dead run (when the wind is directly behind), gybing back towards the leeward mark when you reckon the new course will be another broad reach. If you are ahead of any boats keep an eye on them: don't let them creep up on you and take your wind. If they do, either luff up or steer off to leeward to keep your wind clear. Try to approach the mark on the gybe that you will be rounding on; having to gybe *at* the mark is best avoided. Don't forget to lower the board before rounding!

The final beat will probably be similar to the previous one. Keep trying to improve your speed and assessing how fast you are going in relation to the others.

GOLDEN RULES

- Read the sailing instructions.

- Don't get too far from the start-line.

- Start on starboard tack.

- Keep clear of boats to leeward at the start.

- Try not to sail in dirty wind.

- Approach the windward mark on starboard tack.

- Steer a straight course on each reach.

- Keep going to the finish.

Experiment with sheet tension and the angle that you sail to the wind until you feel you are getting the best speed.

THE FINISH

Make sure that this really is the finish by watching the leaders to be sure that they are stopping. Sail all the way through the finish line: in many clubs the rules prevent you re-crossing the line, so be sure to sail around one of the ends on your way home. Now all you have to do is sign the declaration form, if the rules require it, to say that you completed the course without infringing any of the rules.

WHAT DID YOU THINK OF IT?

By now you will know whether racing is for you. In all probability you will be hooked for life.

Perhaps you may be tempted to think there isn't much to it and that after a few races you'll know it all. However, you will very soon come to realise that there is an infinite amount you still have to learn – and therein lies the true challenge of dinghy racing. The rest of this book should at least serve to open your eyes!

Helming and Crewing Skills

The more you sail your boat, the faster you will be able to sail it.

It's a very good idea to go out and practise, but once you start racing you may well find that practice becomes boring. The advantage of practising over racing is that you can devote more time to thinking about the way you are doing things, and repeat individual manoeuvres until you are happy with them. But when you're racing you are too concerned about losing even one place to risk a new technique. So try to organise some practice.

To begin with, practise in medium winds. If you sail a two-man boat and are lucky enough to have a regular crew, now is the time to work up some teamwork. Remember your crew is not a mind-reader. Only when you have practised and raced together a great deal will you be able to do things without a word. Explain what you intend to do *before* you do it so that you can both be ready to perform in unison.

At first, practise by sailing around two marks lined up with the wind, doing lots of tacks on the beats and plenty of gybes on the runs. Work on your technique, and try to make it fast and fluent.

TACKING

In most dinghies it pays to roll tack the boat in anything but the heaviest of winds. This is achieved by co-ordinating the heel of the boat and its angle to the wind throughout the tack.

- Heel the boat a little more than normal.

- As you begin to push the tiller away, both of you should hike out hard on the weather side.

- Only cross to the other side after the boat has passed through the eye of the wind.

- If you have a jib, hold it aback until the boat is past head to wind; this helps spin the boat round.

- Pull the boat up sharply to the normal sailing angle.

A well-executed roll tack should mean very little loss of speed. In boats with very round sections you can actually speed up when roll tacking excessively. Since it's not legal to come out of a tack faster than you go into it, you may have to subdue your roll tacks! In most boats, and with most beginners, this will definitely not be a problem. Quite obviously, the longer the boat stays head to wind with the sails flapping the more she will slow down, so try to tack quickly.

Prepare to tack...

Push the tiller away...

Roll the boat...

Always try to tack when the boat is going fast, so you maintain sufficient momentum through the turn. Avoid two tacks in quick succession unless they are absolutely essential. Also remember that when sailing in waves you should try to tack on the crest of the wave, when the bow and stern are less deep in the water, rather than in a trough. Experience will help you tack through the correct angle automatically, without ending up too far off the wind or pointing too close to it.

GYBING

You won't gybe as many times in a race as you tack, but a bad gybe in heavy weather can end in a capsize and many lost places. Begin by practising in medium conditions and always remember that you should make the boat gybe when *you* want and not when *it* decides to. In this way you and your crew can be ready to move your weight and steer the boat round at exactly the right moment.

To achieve a smooth gybe it is important that the boat rolls towards the side where you are sitting (the weather side) just before the boom comes across. If the boat is heeling away from you the weather helm that this causes will make bearing off extremely difficult.

Centre the tiller...

Hike out hard...

And sail off.

Assuming that you are not flying a spinnaker, the sequence of events as you turn around the gybe mark should be as follows:

- Take the mainsheet straight from the boom to get a direct pull.

- Bear away as you draw level with the mark, and at the same time lean out.

- Watch the leech of the mainsail. When it lifts you know the boom is ready to come across. Continue bearing away, giving the mainsheet a pull and calling your crew to help the boom across.

- As the boom comes over move quickly to the other side. At the same time reverse the helm to stop the boat continuing round towards the wind and broaching.

- At the same time your crew should also move quickly to the weather side. Unhampered by thoughts of steering he should be able to use his weight to counter the new heeling moment of the mainsail, while sheeting the jib to help reduce weather helm.

If the wind is gusting you will find, rather surprisingly, that it is much easier to gybe when you are going fast. This is because the pressure of wind on the sails is lightest when the boat is moving quickly away from the wind. This lets the boom to come over more easily. Confidence is the hallmark of gybing in a blow!

BEATING

You must learn to sail to windward by second nature. There are many decisions to be taken during a beat: has the wind shifted; should we tack; which way is paying; where are the competition heading? While you're thinking about that lot you're sailing the boat through the water on automatic pilot.

You will discover that as you pinch (sail too close to the wind) a number of things happen: the sails begin to lift near the luff (leading edge), the boat starts to heel towards you, and you will actually hear the boat slowing up as the wave sound against the hull diminishes.

Even with your eyes closed you should be aware that you are pinching. Bearing too far off the wind is rather less obvious, so the art of beating is to sail closer to the wind until you get the 'messages' that tell you to bear off.

Apart from accurate steering you will need to pay attention to sail trim. The main and jib need to be pulled in fairly tightly so the boat can point quite close to the wind. Generally, pull in the mainsheet until the top telltale on the leech (the one by the top batten) breaks. The tighter you pull down on the mainsheet the more the mast will bend, flattening the sail. Also, the tension down the leech will reduce its twist. The conditions (wind strength and waves) will dictate the correct sail shape for beating.

- A flat sail is required for strong winds because a deeply-cambered sail will produce too great a side force (and heeling moment) as well as increased drag.

- Medium winds require a fuller sail.

- Very light winds once again need a fairly flat sail so that the wind can flow across it without turbulence. Achieve this by inducing mast bend without much sheet tension so that a degree of twist remains in the sail. This is best done by removing chocks at deck level, raking the spreaders aft or prebending under rig tension (see pages 70/71, Tuning).

Jib sheeting is also important. Too tight and the sail will be too flat, too loose and the leech curls which reduces power and stops the boat pointing. Generally, ease the jib sheet in lighter winds, moving the fairlead forward to prevent too much twisting off at the top. Sheet harder in medium winds, with the fairlead central. Move the fairlead aft in strong winds and play the jibsheet to keep the boat on her feet – that is, let the sheet out a bit in gusts.

It's a good idea to attach telltales to the luff of your jib. These are short wool streamers about eight centimetres (three inches) long, fixed at intervals on each side of the jib about ten centimetres (four inches) behind the luff. Telltales act as guides for steering and also for sheeting angle. When you are sailing closehauled at the optimum angle to the wind the telltales should stream back horizontally on both sides of the jib. As you luff closer to the wind the telltales on the weather side will fly upwards. If the upper telltale breaks first then the sail is too twisted and the fairlead may need moving forward. But if the lower one breaks first the jib sheet is too tight or the fairlead needs to come aft to induce more twist.

Many helmsmen use the telltales all the time as a guide to good windward sailing; for others general 'feel and heel' are a more precise guide. But if you see the leeward telltales break, you are definitely too far off the wind.

Beating in light winds

Because side forces are no problem in light winds, use full sails to increase drive. (In very light winds full sails don't work because the airstream is too weak to follow a large curve.)

Pointing close to the wind is no longer important: keeping the boat moving is the top priority. Choose tacks that will take you towards increased wind, as indicated by wavelets on the water. Move around the boat slowly, if you need to move at all, because violent movements will shake the wind out of the sails. Disregard the normal need to keep the boat flat, allowing her to heel about 5–10 degrees. This is advantageous in two ways: first, it helps keep the sails full by gravity alone; second, the wetted surface area on most dinghies is reduced. Sitting forward in the boat also reduces wetted area. Smooth roll tacks are essential in these conditions.

Beating in strong winds

As the wind strength increases beyond the point where you can hold the boat flat by hiking hard, you will need to lose power to prevent excessive heeling. If you let the boat heel you will need to pull hard on the tiller to counter the increased weather helm, which causes drag

Keep the boat upright in medium to strong winds – you'll go faster that way.

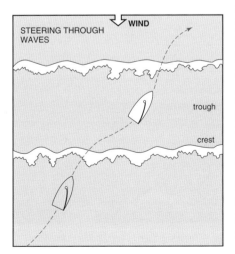

STEERING THROUGH WAVES

WIND

trough

crest

and slows the boat. Also, since the hull is designed to travel through the water upright, resistance increases as she heels. Keep the boat dead upright. Let the jib-sheet out a little.

Flatten the main by:

1 Pulling hard (very hard) on the vang (kicking strap).

2 Removing chocks from in front of the mast at deck level (this lets the mast bend).

It is also a good idea to rake the mast further aft than normal; this reduces the overlap between the jib and main and reduces power. Now all you have to do is sail the boat to windward, keeping her flat by playing the mainsheet in and out. If a gust hits you, let out an arm's length of mainsheet and bear away a little to pick up speed. Once the boat is motoring, pull in the sheet again.

In boats such as the Laser, which rely on an extremely bent mast to maintain a sensible sail shape, easing the mainsheet lets the mast straighten and results in a fuller sail (despite a tight vang, which will always stretch). In these boats an alternative method of depowering is preferable, such as feathering.

Feathering is a technique of 'pinching' very close to the wind, causing the front edge of the sail to lift, then bearing off before the boat slows too much. Successive luffs have the advantage of ensuring you are sailing close to the wind as well as helping to keep the boat upright. It is a technique that needs to be practised, and it is only effective in smooth water.

In waves, the beginner is advised to ease the sheet a good deal and sail well off the wind. Remember to sit close to your crew (if you have one) to reduce pitching (bow and stern going up and down); indeed any weight in the bow or stern is detrimental in waves.

Steering in waves is an art; keep the tiller and main-sheet in constant motion, luffing up (and pulling in the sheet) as the boat goes up each wave and bearing away (and letting out the sheet) as the bow reaches each crest. Pick up speed down the back of the wave before luffing up for the next.

REACHING

Many feel that after a long hard beat the reach is the time to relax. We're sorry to tell you that the reverse is true: if you work hard you can gain many places on the reach, particularly in planing conditions and in big fleets.

Good reaching speed relies on careful sail trim and on keeping the boat flat.

Ease both main and jib until they lift on the luff, then sheet in a little. Keep trying this sequence to ensure that you haven't missed a windshift.

You need only moderate vang (kicking strap) tension to stop the boom lifting and the upper sail being freed off too much.

In the absence of other considerations, such as wind changes or other boats, try to sail the direct rhumb line between the marks. A curved course can add many boat lengths of distance. Be careful not to steer too high a course: if you line up the bow with the mark you will automatically sail too high (see photo). Make an allowance for this by 'pointing' well below the mark.

As a gust arrives, ease sheets and bear off a little. This helps in three ways:

- In the increased wind of a gust your speed does not decrease much as you bear away. Later, in the inevitable lull, you can *increase* speed by luffing back towards the rhumb line.

- You offset the immediate heeling force.

- Most important, you carry the gust longer as you sail down with it.

As the gust passes, pull in the sheets and luff back up to increase your speed and take you to windward so you reach the next gust sooner.

Always keep the boat flat so that its planing surface is horizontal. Sit out hard, bearing off at the same time if

This 420 is reaching straight for the buoy, although the sightline through the forestay suggests otherwise.

the boat begins to heel. Only in very light weather is a little heel permissible to reduce wetted area and keep the sails full.

The centreboard should be about half up. This reduces wetted area and also reduces weather helm, while still countering the sideforces.

Reaching in waves

You will need to move aft a little to keep the bow above the waves. Take the mainsheet straight from the boom. As you reach the top of a wave bear away, sheet in and try to plane down it.

Sheeting in is essential to take account of the apparent wind that comes forward as you accelerate. These are probably the most exciting conditions you can race in, and practice will bring its rewards.

RUNNING

Running in light winds

Because the sail plan of most boats is unbalanced, when running it is usually a good idea to heel the boat 5–10 degrees to weather to get the centre of effort of the sail over the centreline of the boat. (Boats with

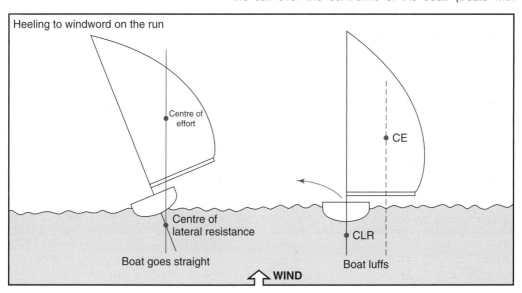

Heeling to windword on the run

Centre of effort

CE

Centre of lateral resistance

CLR

Boat goes straight

Boat luffs

WIND

spinnakers are better balanced.) As a result less rudder is needed to keep the boat running straight (every time you use the rudder on a reach or a run the brakes go on). With most dinghies this weather heel will also reduce wetted area.

On a run it helps for the helmsman and crew to sit out on opposite sides. Their moment of inertia helps to prevent any roll starting. (In non-technical terms, the wind has to raise one of the crew if it wants to heel the boat.)

Running in strong winds

Though rather less exciting than the reach, a heavy weather run can be very demanding indeed. Your boat may become rather unstable and develop a pronounced roll, while in a seaway she may try to nosedive.

When you round a leeward mark it is usually preferable to come in wide and exit close to that mark when other boats are in the vicinity.

You can greatly reduce these problems by steering firmly, sheeting correctly and moving your weight aft. Don't allow the mainsail out too far! If you do, any twist in the sail will allow the head to swing forward of the mast, producing a force to weather that makes you roll. So if you find yourself rolling to weather, pull in the mainsheet. If you heel to leeward let out the mainsheet. Don't raise the board too high – its depth in the water has a distinct damping effect.

Don't sit too far forward if you think the boat may nose-dive. Sheeting in a little also helps by reducing forces at the top of the mast.

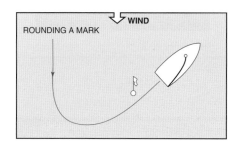

ROUNDING MARKS

Like all other 'set pieces', mark rounding needs practice. It is usualy best to approach the mark wide, then turn slowly and smoothly round it, exiting very close to the buoy. In this way you avoid losing too much speed round the turn, and start the next leg in a good tactical position, free to carry on or tack.

STARTING

A crowded startline is no place to find that you're weak at slowing, stopping, flapping or accelerating. Practise on your own, well before the race, using a buoy. Reach up to it, then point into the wind and slow down. Try to 'hang' with your bow just off the buoy for two minutes at least. If you find you're going forwards, push out the boom. If you're drifting back, pull in the jib. If you're stuck in irons (head to wind), jerk the tiller towards you several times, or push out the boom.

Try sailing backwards in case you need to reverse over the startline – go head to wind, push out the boom and hold it against the shrouds. Then steer backwards (point the tiller the way you want the bow to swing).

Practise sailing up to the line as slowly as possible, with your sails flapping.

Now practise accelerating off the line. Turn the boat onto a close reach, gradually squeeze in the sails and luff slowly to close-hauled. Jerk the boat level, and

If you get stuck head to wind, push out the boom or back the jib to make the boat bear away.

Push out the boom to stop.

you're away. The whole process should take about ten seconds.

Finally, set up a ten-metre (33-foot) startline between two buoys, and practise starting through it giving yourself a two-minute and a one-minute 'gun'.

GOLDEN RULES

- Practice makes perfect.

- Keep the boat flat.

- On a beat, sheet the main so that the top telltale just breaks.

- Play the jibsheet – a couple of inches makes all the difference.

- Sit forward in light winds.

- You need flat sails when beating in very light and in strong winds.

- On a reach luff in the lulls and bear away in the gusts.

- Heel the boat to windward on a run.

- To round a mark, approach it wide and leave it close.

- Practise strategy: a crowded startline is no place to learn!

Boat Preparation and Equipment

You will by now have discovered that not everything on your boat works one hundred percent. Little niggling things that you are prepared to put up with when cruising become major problems when you're in a race: jamb cleats that don't, a rudder that unexpectedly come up half way down the reach, and a mainsheet that don't run smoothly.

Once you become at all serious about racing you must also take boat preparation seriously. After each race you need to make a list of all the problems, then find the time to rectify them before you race again. If you don't have the time to attend to the problems immediately, keep a running list of all items requiring attention, then have a blitz. The occasional windless day spent sorting out the boat can be very satisfying in itself.

But even before you sort out the gear, make sure the hull and foils are not letting you down.

HULL PREPARATION

While the wind acting on the sails provides the force to move your boat forward, the friction of the water on the hull retards it. If you can reduce the friction to a minimum you will attain the best possible speed in any given conditions.

Turn your boat upside down and inspect the underwater surfaces. You should do this frequently anyway. Out of sight, out of mind is not a good policy: you may have damaged the hull without knowing it.

Apart from maintaining a smooth finish to the bottom it is very important on wooden boats to make certain that no bare wood has become exposed. Most modern wooden boats are epoxy coated. Once scratched, water may soak in causing both serious deterioration of the hull and an increase in weight. GRP soaks up water too, so any damage to the gel-coat needs immediate attention.

On the question of hull weight, you should at least be aware of how heavy your boat is. Nothing more sophisticated than two sets of bathroom scales – one supporting each end, their readings added together – are needed to get a good idea of true weight. A hull weight of more than five percent above the minimum allowed should be a cause for concern. Less than this is probably acceptable unless the boat is new or you are likely to be discouraged by knowing that your boat is overweight.

Any rough edges should be smoothed off with a rough file or sandpaper. Use fine wet-and-dry sandpaper even after the final coat of paint is applied if you are really keen!

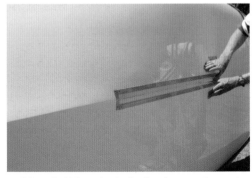

A well designed sailcloth centreboard gasket allows the water to drain out aft.

In most classes slot gaskets are allowed, to reduce the drag caused by water entering and leaving the centreboard case. If yours are made of rubber or mylar they may need replacing. Heavy sailcloth lasts longer.

THE FOILS

A smooth finish to the centreboard and rudder is even more important than the hull finish. Most of the hull moves through turbulent water, but the foils move through relatively smooth water and the percentage effect on speed reduction is much greater. Plastic Padding or similar filler offers a quick solution to the chips that inevitably occur.

When you are smoothing off the foils, make sure that the front edge is well rounded, and the trailing edge is sharp (or slightly square). But do check that your class rules allow you to do all this.

MAST AND RIGGING

If you have bought a new boat you should have chosen a mast whose section is most commonly used by the fleet leaders (in many one-design classes you will have no option anyway).

Now you need to set the mast up. Provided it has shrouds, you have control over the rake of the mast (angle) and the tension of the rig. Note that the shroud lengths control the rake, while the jib halyard tension controls the rig tension (the tension in the jib luff *and* shrouds). If the mast has spreaders, then their length and angle may be adjusted to control the bend in the mast.

The beginner should try and copy the precise set-up of one of the more successful boats; indeed you should be able to find someone who will be pleased to set up your boat for you. After all, if they are quite good they will not expect you, a beginner, to start beating them, and they have little to lose by helping you. So rule one is: seek advice on mast set-up.

But if help is unforthcoming, here is a rough do-it-yourself guide.

Always make sure that the forestay (if you have one) is looser than the jib luff.

Rig tension

The first thing to do is set up the rig fairly tight by pulling on the jib halyard. You can't assess the mast rake or bend until the tension is on. (Note that you set up the boat with the jib up but the mainsail down.) It is very important to be aware that the forestay on a dinghy is simply there to stop the mast falling down when the jib is removed. (If the class rules permit you might consider dispensing with the forestay altogether, using the halyard to hold up the mast after you take the jib down.)

It is of vital importance that the jib luff is tighter than the forestay. Otherwise the jib will sag, and this will introduce excessive fullness (camber) into the sail. This adversely affects how close to the wind you can point on the beat. (To overcome the distraction of a loose forestay waving around, a short piece of shock cord is often used to keep it artificially 'tight'.)

Rig tension is controlled by the precise setting of the jib halyard – tensions of between 90–160 kg (200–350 lbs) are typical. Read Lawrie Smith's *Tuning your Dinghy* for an in depth treatment, and buy a tension gauge when you get really serious. For now, see that the jib halyard is very tight, so you get a good 'twang' when you pluck a shroud.

Mast rake

Mast rake (the fore and aft angle of the mast in the boat) is controlled primarily by the length of the main shrouds (and to a much lesser extent by the jib halyard setting). This is measured by setting the boat up level in both fore-and-aft and lateral planes and hanging a heavy weight on the main halyard. Racing experience on the water will produce the best setting. A good starting point will be around 20 cm (8 inches).

The rake of the mast will have an effect on the balance of the boat. A well set-up dinghy *when sailed level* should carry slight weather helm. That is, if you let go of the tiller when beating, the boat will steer itself into the wind. If the boat does not do this, or worse still bears away, then more weather helm is required which

Measure spreader deflection from the mast to a straight edge laid between the tips.

To use a rig tension meter, hook it on the luff wire, pull it so the pointer reaches mark A, and read off the value by the wire (B).

Measure the mast rake by stretching a tape from the masthead to the transom.

Alternatively, measure between the black band and a plumbline.

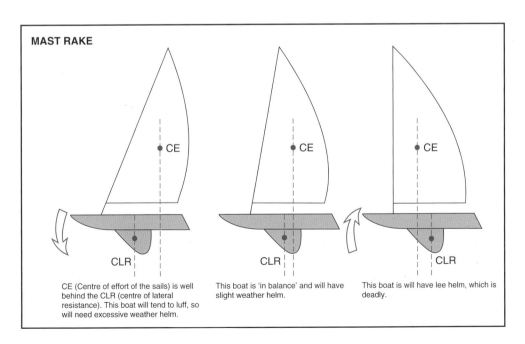

MAST RAKE

CE (Centre of effort of the sails) is well behind the CLR (centre of lateral resistance). This boat will tend to luff, so will need excessive weather helm.

This boat is 'in balance' and will have slight weather helm.

This boat is will have lee helm, which is deadly.

you can achieve, up to a point, by increasing the rake of the mast.

Conversely too much weather helm, which needs a larger rudder deflection to hold the boat straight and has a slowing effect, can be remedied by moving the mast more upright. You will notice when sailing that too much heel results in excessive weather helm, so always sail the boat as near upright as you can.

Sideways lean

When you have the boat chocked and are checking the mast rake, make sure that the mast isn't leaning over sideways. To do this take the shackle on the main halyard to the base of one shroud, hold it there and cleat the halyard tight. Now move the shackle over to the other shroud; it should touch the base when you pull down with the same tension. If it doesn't, adjust the shroud lengths until the mast is vertical.

Mast bend

Mast bend is a key factor in tuning, and is fully covered on page 70. For the time being, angle the spreaders aft until there is a five centimetre (two inch) bend in the middle of the mast: you can judge this by pulling the main halyard tightly down to the gooseneck and judging the distance between the (bent) mast and the (straight) halyard.

Make sure that the spreaders are symmetrical by measuring from the tip of each to the centre of the transom.

Jib fairlead

With the jib set up on land you can check the position of the jib fairlead. The vertical jib sheeting angle is determined by the fore-and-aft position of the fairlead. The jib sheet should approximately bisect the angle of the jib clew.

GEAR AND SYSTEMS

Don't be psyched by boats in the dinghy park that have string and pulleys all over them. You can enter a 49er for the Olympic trials next year – but for the time being just

Mast bend can also be controlled by varying the number of chocks in front of the mast.

make sure that the few *essential* controls are fully adjustable, and that each of these systems works properly.

Mainsheet

Make sure the mainsheet runs freely through its blocks. If you use a ratchet block adjust it so the grip suits you. Make sure the mainsheet cleat angle is right so the sheet can be released quickly when a gust strikes.

Jibsheet

In a similar way, make sure the jib fairleads are smooth and that the cleats are properly angled so the crew doesn't waste time cleating and uncleating the sheet.

Vang (kicking strap)

Once you are sailing this is the primary control for tuning the mainsail. It must be sufficiently powerful to enable you to pull the boom right down when the wind is in the sail. If the class rules allow, the control lines should be divided and led to the helmsman at each side deck.

Jib halyard

The jib halyard usually controls the rig tension, so this system must work one hundred percent. If you only

Two ways of increasing the purchase on the vang – a cascade system of blocks (left) and a gnav strut system (right).

use a highfield lever it must not be allowed to slip. A more powerful system such as a multi-purchase 16–1 set-up will do the job with a lot less effort on your part.

Check that all the halyard sheaves in the mast are well lubricated. It's surprising how much easier the halyards will run after a squirt of lubricant such as WD40. This is vital for the jib halyard, but the spinnaker halyard must run freely too. Check that the halyards are not twisted round each other in the mast.

The centreboard control

The centreboard also needs an effective control system. When beating you usually want the board fully down – if it comes up of its own accord it can be very annoying. On a reach you will need to raise the board a little. Some quite complicated arrangements can be installed, particularly to raise the board when it is under great side pressure, but to begin with a simple system of retaining it where you want it will be adequate.

The rudder and tiller

You will have either a fixed rudder or one that can be lifted for launching and landing in shallow water. A properly-made fixed rudder has the advantage of complete rigidity and is preferable if you are confident you can sail without a rudder until you reach deep water.

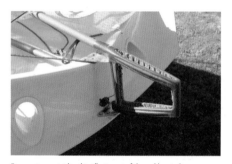

For maximum rigidity this tiller is part of the rudder stock.

A lifting rudder can be satisfactory, but you will find when fast reaching that the rudder blade will rake aft, giving an unacceptably heavy helm, unless the rudder is fixed in its vertical position by some very positive method. A piece of elastic is just not up to the job. Even a pull-down cord is likely to stretch the quarter-inch or so that will give an unacceptable aft rake. If the class rules allow, by far the best solution is to use a wooden dowel pin or at least a metal split pin to locate it in the fully down position. Wood has the advantage of breaking off if you do ground the rudder unexpectedly; this is preferable to pulling the transom out!

This connection to the tiller extension is a universal joint.

The tiller and tiller extension should also be considered carefully. A positive joint between the tiller and the rudder stock is essential; any slop causes a loss of 'feel'.

GOLDEN RULES

- Keep a checklist *in* the boat of things that don't work.

- Turn your boat over often to inspect the bottom.

- Your boat should be light.

- The shrouds control mast rake.

- The jib halyard controls rig tension.

- The jib halyard must be tighter than the forestay.

- The spreaders control mast bend, as do the chocks at deck level.

- Mast rake should be about 20 centimetres (8 inches), to give slight weather helm *when the boat is level*.

- The mast must not lean sideways.

- All controls *must work*.

- Keep the boat dry.

- Check screws and bolts for tightness.

The best solution is a one-piece arrangement in which tiller and stock are permanently connected together. The extension-to-tiller connection should be of the universal joint variety. (A rubber version is good too, but it needs periodic checking. When a split is noticed, that's your cue to renew it!)

Bailers

Another area of frustration is a leaking bailer. Make certain that the bailers are locked up when you first launch, and then check that no water is seeping in; it is much more difficult to detect a small leak when there is water swilling around in the bottom. If you have a problem it can be almost certainly rectified with a new gasket. Always remember that water is heavy and quite a small amount in the boat means you will be carrying lots of unnecessary weight. A bucketful of water weighs about 9 kg (20 lbs). Try pouring a bucketful of water into your boat – it doesn't look a lot.

Carrying a sizeable sponge is recommended, particularly on those days when you can't expect to go fast enough for the self bailers to work – water has a habit of getting into your boat some way or other even if only from your boots as you climb aboard.

GENERAL MAINTENANCE

From time to time you should go over your boat with a screwdriver and spanner, checking screws and nuts that may have come loose. In particular, the toestrap screws, the screws or bolts securing the rudder fittings and the fairleads need checking.

It's a very good idea to carry a screwdriver, pair of pliers, knife, shackle, and short lengths of line on your boat at all times. It's surprising how often one of these will come to your rescue.

Tactics

533 is blanketing 530 by getting between her and the wind. 530 will have to drop back or tack to find clear air.

Tactics are about manoeuvring against other boats. The idea is to position yourself so you have an advantage, and leave your competitors at a disadvantage.

The very presence of your boat will affect the path the wind takes, and you can use this to affect other boats. This is very important since you will often want to slow down an opponent and you will always need to avoid being slowed by someone else.

WIND SHADOW

Perhaps the most obvious way you can slow a competitor is by taking his wind (blanketing him). On a run the leading boat is very vulnerable to this tactic, since a boat immediately behind can effectively steal her wind. In the diagram on page 44 the leading boat (A) should luff or gybe to find clean wind.

On a reach the wind shadow comes into effect as a boat overtakes to windward. To prevent this the leeward boat (C) should luff well before the blanketing action begins. The disadvantage of luffing is that you may be forced to sail a much greater distance if the boat behind (D) continues to luff.

Even when beating there is a wind shadow, although now the cone is much narrower (boats E and F in the

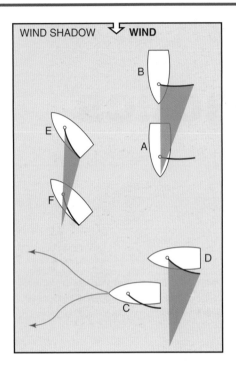

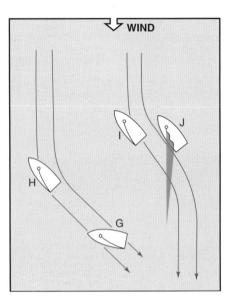

diagram.) However, when you are beating an equally important phenomenon comes into effect: dirty wind.

DIRTY WIND

When beating, your boat not only blankets the area immediately to leeward but also bends the wind and generally disturbs its smooth path. So when one boat is beating ahead of another, the one behind (G in the diagram) experiences a heading, cut up airflow. It is said to be in the *hopeless position*.

In either of the above cases the trailing boat (F or G) must tack away to seek clean wind.

LEE-BOW EFFECT

In this situation the leeward boat (I in the diagram) is ahead of the wind shadow of the windward boat (J) and is close enough for her sails to bend the wind onto the leeward side of J's sails.

530 (left) is lee-bowing 533, which will soon fall behind.

A successful luff by 4 fends off a challenge by 3.

Unless the leeward boat is slower or being sailed badly she will draw ahead. The weather boat must tack away or she will fall behind.

The leeward boat is said to be in a safe leeward position, and the windward boat is being lee-bowed.

THE START

Unlike a long-distance race in athletics, in yacht racing the sprint comes at the start. Because most races begin on a beat, the boats that are ahead just after the start blanket and lee-bow those behind them. As a result the leaders gradually pull away, so a poor start can cost you the race. And the more boats in a race, the more important a good start is, and a good position at the first mark.

Although it is helpful to cross the startline within two or three seconds of the starting signal and with good speed, the essential thing is to be ahead of the other boats in the immediate vicinity. Also, if the startline is more than 25 metres (80 feet) long and not set squarely to the wind, your position on that line is very important.

In championship races where a hundred or more boats are starting, the line may be several hundred metres long. If you start at the wrong end of a line that is biased only five degrees, you have to sail a lot further to the first mark than someone who sets off from the favoured end. In the diagram, K will come out ahead of L.

But don't be misled into assuming that, because mark W is closer to the starboard end of the line (as the crow flies), starting at this end means you will sail the shortest distance to the mark. As long as the first leg is a beat (so you need to make at least one tack) the position of the windward mark is irrelevant when you're deciding where to start: all that matters is the bias of the startline to the wind. With the wind biased to the port end, the boats starting from that end sail the shorter distance. If the starboard end is favoured, boats beginning at that end should come out ahead.

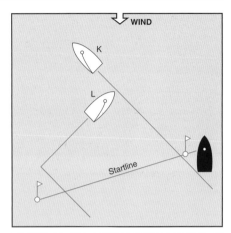

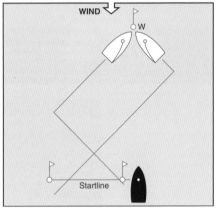

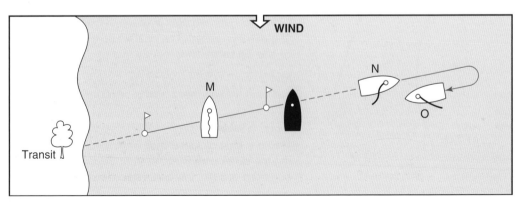

For a quick check on the line, point the boat head to wind. The bow points towards the favoured end.

Determining which end of the line is biased

In yachts that are heavy enough to carry way for several seconds when pointed directly into the wind, a judgement can be made by sailing up to the line, luffing until the boom remains on the centreline and then deciding which end of the line your bow is biased towards. In the diagram, M's bow points somewhat towards the committee boat, so that's the end to start.

A very precise method of assessing the line in a light dinghy is to sail your boat along the extension of the line (rather than along the line itself – this is more accurate and the water is less congested). First sail in one direction. Let the jib flap, then ease out the mainsheet until it is half flapping and half drawing (like N in the diagram). Then turn the boat around *without altering the mainsheet's trim* and sail along the extension of the line in the opposite direction. If the sail now fills you are sailing away from the upwind direction (like O in the diagram). If it luffs more you are pointing towards the upwind direction.

Another method of assessing the line can be used on a dinghy or a yacht, providing there is a compass on board.

Sail close-hauled on port, then on starboard, noting the heading in each case. The wind direction lies mid-way between the two headings. Then sail along the line,

Assessing the line. Letting the jib flap throughout, sail along the line with half the main flapping (left). Tack, but do not adjust the mainsheet. The main now fills, so the buoy end of the line is favoured.

or better still its extension, and determine its bearing. Usually it will *not* be at 90 degrees to the wind direction, and it is now a relatively simple matter to work out which end of the line is upwind. The disadvantage of this method is that it can take some time, and if the wind is shifting or the line is changed (it can be moved any time before the five-minute gun) you may not have the time.

Having determined if one end of the line is favoured, your next decision is where on the line you should start. In the absence of other factors, such as wanting to go a particular way up the first beat, try to start at or near the biased end of the line.

Using a stopwatch

Most books tell you to start your stopwatch at the five-minute signal, check it at the four-minute signal, and then count down to the start. In practice this is impossible, because you don't know when the five-minute signal is going to be made.

By all means start the watch at the five-minute signal (you'll be a bit late). Plan your manoeuvring so you are near the committee boat with four-and-a-half minutes to go, and then zero your watch. You should be able to hear the officer of the day (OOD) counting down, and you can then get the timing exactly.

If you have a watch with both a stopwatch and a timer mode, use the stopwatch for the first half minute, then flip to timer just before the four-minute signal and hit it right on the bottom.

Note that the four-minute signal is the key – if there's any discrepancy you assume the four-minute signal was correct, not the five. You are not racing until the four-minute signal.

Starting mid-line

If the fleet is large, aim to start a little way from the extreme ends – there should be more room near the middle. Try to approach the line with sails flapping on a close reach for the last minute (more if it's a very big fleet), being particularly careful to avoid dropping down on boats to leeward that have the right of way. Luff boats to weather and attempt to create space to leeward so that you can bear off a little with about 15 seconds to go and hit the line at some speed. If you just sheet in with five seconds to go and everyone around you is moving they will leave you for dead.

Judging how far you are behind the line is difficult in a large fleet: you need to keep up with the first rank of starters, yet not be so far forward that you will be spotted as a premature starter.

Even when you can see both ends of the line it is difficult to judge whether you are on it or not unless you are near one end. In fact you always think you are over well before you are actually on the line. Have you ever noticed that when you finish a race the race committee always seems to be late in giving you a finishing signal? In fact they're not – it's just that you think you're on the line well before you are.

Take a transit on the startline – here the peak of the house lines up with the outer distance mark.

This is how to judge accurately your distance from the line. You remember that you're supposed to be reaching up and down the extension of the line assessing the bias? At the same time, look for a distant object in line with the end of the starting line (in the photo, a peak of a house serves this purpose). This object is your transit. When you're approaching the line to start, move forwards until the appropriate end lines up with your transit once more.

At this point you will know that you are right on the line. You will probably be surprised how far forward you can go, but you will learn to trust your transit (provided the buoy marking the end of the line isn't drifting!) A transit beyond the port end is best, but if nothing is visible a transit the other way will do. As you make your start keep the transit in mind. Until it begins to line up with the mark, there is no need to begin holding back.

Another useful and quick way of determining if you are still behind the line is the 'tiller method'. Sail along the line, point your bow at one end of the line, centre your tiller and look back along it. If the tiller is pointing back behind the other end of the line, you are still behind the line. If the tiller is pointing 'over' the line, you're over. This method is more revealing than you imagine. Try it out!

Remember good starts can be vital. Knowing how close you are to the line when others don't is extremely useful.

How do I make a starboard-end start?

Sail slowly, and as close to the wind as possible, so you reach the windward end of the line with the gun. Boats to windward have no rights and are forced out. Boats to leeward can't touch you – you are already sailing as close to the wind as possible.

How do I make a port-end start?

Aim to be at the port end of the line with two minutes to go. Reach towards the fleet, which will be sitting on the line, flapping, about 100 metres away. Tack just before the first boat, then sail as slowly as possible towards the port end of the line. With ten seconds to go sheet in and cross the line at full speed.

THE GATE START

For some years now gate starts have been used at large championships as an alternative. The success of this radical system can be measured by the number of otherwise conservative classes that have adopted it.

How it works

The gate start is a dynamic starting method. This is to say that the starting line is changing all the time as boats in their turn begin to race. At its simplest, one chosen competitor (the pathfinder) sails on port tack across the whole fleet, followed by a motorboat (the gate launch). Each boat starts in turn under the gate launch's stern. In this way each boat will have a start equal to everyone else, so long as each boat just clears the launch's stern, and the pathfinder and gate launch travel at a constant speed and direction while the gate is opening (that is to say, the wind stays steady in both strength and direction).

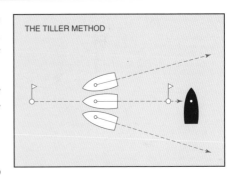

THE TILLER METHOD

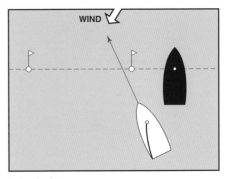

Starboard end start

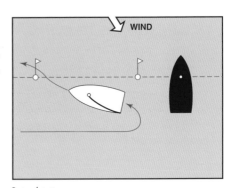

Port end start

If a significant change in wind strength or direction takes place the race committee should abandon the start, but smaller changes can be tolerated and still give a much fairer start than can be reasonably expected from a conventional line start.

A championship gate start is rather more complicated than described above, but the principle is the same.

The procedure

The starting signals are made from a separate committee boat. Approximately 15 seconds before the start signal is due the pathfinder, followed closely by the gate launch, proceeds on a close-hauled port tack away from the vicinity of the committee boat. Three seconds before the start a free-floating buoy is dropped from the stern of the gate launch. At the starting signal boats may sail across the imaginary line between the centre of the gate launch and the centre of the floating buoy. In addition to the gate launch there is usually another powered craft (the guard launch), which positions herself level with and to leeward of the pathfinder and protects her from any collisions with wayward yachts not obeying the rules. This entourage continues for approximately two to three minutes before the pathfinder is given permission to tack or continue as she sees fit. After the pathfinder has tacked off the gate launch will continue at the same speed and on the same course for a further minute or so before stopping and floating for approximately a further minute and signalling the closing of the gate. These times may be shortened when a smaller fleet is being started.

Techniques of gate starting

Various decisions need to be taken as to how to start. Should you go early or late? This will depend on a number of considerations.

Is the pathfinder likely to be faster on the beat than you? Since she is usually the boat that finished tenth in the previous race, if you are a beginner then going late will probably be to your advantage.

Also, strategic considerations such as which way you want to go up the beat will determine when to go. If you expect the wind to veer (move in a clockwise direction) going late will pay off – or vice versa if you think it will back. The current may also affect your decision.

Once you have decided where you will start, you need to put yourself in a position to make a good approach. The best way to do this is to sail close-hauled on port tack away from the committee boat area for a prede-termined time, say two to two-and-a-half minutes if you choose to start late. You are following the course that the pathfinder will sail. Now bear off onto a broad reach for another minute, then tack and stop with your sails flapping. You are now approximately one to one-and-a-half minutes of starboard-tack beating from your start, if the wind is steady. However, you should expect to take at least twice this time to cover the distance as you slowly close-reach towards the gate boat.

This is the critical time where good technique pays dividends. You know from your watch when the start is due. You may not see the pathfinder at the moment the gun goes if you are starting late. However, you should soon spot the entourage of pathfinder, gate launch, guard boat and gaggle of starters proceeding along their course. Once you have seen them, make sure you are always well forward of the position that will enable you to reach them at full speed.

Remember it will be easy to slow up by easing sheets and luffing, virtually to a halt if necessary. Never, never be panicked into bearing off because you are worried that you may arrive too early. This will only speed you up and ensure that you do arrive early. You will also hit the boats to leeward, as boat P in the diagram is about to discover.

As with a conventional start try to maintain a gap to leeward by 'holding up' competitors to weather of you, so that as you approach the gate boat you can bear off, gain speed and start close under her stern with full speed. Q in the diagram is doing this. Remember the gate boat is moving so don't aim for her stern but

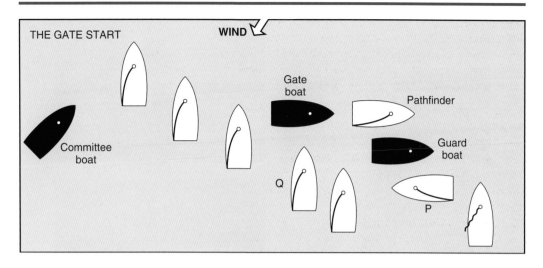

THE GATE START

WIND

Gate boat

Pathfinder

Committee boat

Guard boat

Q

P

instead further forward. Just keep your eyes open and you won't hit her or anyone to leeward. However, any collision with the pathfinder, gate boat or guard boat results in instant disqualification, so do watch it!

TACTICS ON THE BEAT

Your speed will be low if you are in someone's wind shadow, or if there is another boat dead ahead or lee-bowing you. If this is the case, look over your shoulder to see if you are clear to tack. If you have room, tack immediately, but if there is a pile of boats to weather you may have to carry on for a bit. Sometimes it pays to bear away a little or even slow down to let them by, then tack into clear air.

In this case you will have made a poor start, so tack onto port and duck the whole fleet. (Since they are almost in line at this stage, you will only lose a length or two.) Once in clear air, tack back onto starboard.

Port v starboard

There will be many times on the beat when you find yourself on a collision course with a boat on the opposite tack.

If you are on port tack you must keep clear, but you can choose whether you bear away behind your rival (don't

MEETING ON OPPOSITE TACKS

WIND

tack on lee bow

or bear away

port tack

starboard tack

4 is asking for trouble approaching the windward mark on port. She must give way to 3 who is on starboard, and must not tack too close. In the event she hits 3 while still tacking, she must do a two turn penalty.

forget to ease the sheets a bit, to make this easier) or tack shortly before you hit her. The rules require you to complete your tack a short distance away from the starboard tack boat; she must have time to avoid you, beginning her avoiding action no earlier than the time you completed your tack. Note that if you tack at just the right moment, you may end up lee-bowing your opponent. But if you get it wrong, she may hit you or sail over the top of you. Sailing's like that.

If you are on starboard you have the right of way. However, power confers responsibility: you must keep a straight course so that the port-tack boat has a chance to keep clear. Even if there is a windshift, you must keep going in a straight line until she is clear of you.

When ahead

It's a general principle that if you are ahead of another boat, and want to stay there, keep between her and the next mark. She then has to sail around your hull to pass you, which means she is not only sailing further but is doing so in your wake. That should keep her back!

On a beat this tactic is even more effective because you can hold the rival boat in your windshadow. If you're really determined to keep her behind you can cover. This involves staying on her wind by tacking every time she does. But be careful – covering slows you down and other boats can sneak by while you're duelling.

TACTICS ON THE REACH

The quickest way down the reach is a straight line from one mark to the next. However, if your rivals let you sail this course, you're lucky! The problem is that overtaking boats (R in the diagram) push up to windward. The boats to leeward (S) get nervous about their wind being stolen and steer high also. The result is that everyone sails an enormous arc (X), losing ground on the leaders.

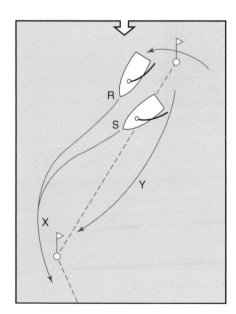

You have to decide whether or not to go on the 'great circle'; the alternative is to sail a leeward path (Y). You have to go down far enough to avoid the blanketing effect of the boats to windward – but usually you will sail a shorter distance than they do. You will also get the inside turn at the gybe mark. You can go for the leeward route on the second reach too, but this time you will be on the outside at the turn.

To protect your wind you are allowed to luff, that is turn towards the wind, giving the windward boat time to keep clear. You can go right up to head to wind, and the windward boat has to keep clear. Usually, a little luff in good time will prevent someone behind from trying to roll over you.

You can continue to luff until the overlap is broken (until the line through the windward boat's transom is ahead of you).

If you are doing the overtaking, work well to windward before you try to get through another boat's wind. You then have plenty of time to see the luff coming, and keep clear.

TACTICS ON THE RUN

Your 'ideal' course to the leeward mark is often impossible in the presence of other boats. If another boat is blanketing you (if her burgee is pointing straight at your mast) luff a little into clear air. If she continues to blanket you, and you don't want to veer off course too far, then gybe so as to go for clear air on the other side. You can easily gybe back later.

If you find yourself behind another boat you can of course blanket her. Simply sail right up behind (blanketing is effective at four mast lengths, but becomes deadly as you get even nearer) and swerve to one side at the last moment. Passing to leeward is often the best, as she is then unable to luff you. And it's an especially good choice if it gives you the inside turn at the leeward mark.

TACTICS AT THE FINISH

If you have one boat close behind, cover her to the finish.

If you're level-pegging with one or more boats try to avoid the position of T in the diagram: you can't tack for the line until U does and you'll come in behind her. Try to manoeuvre yourself into the controlling position, and hold well on until you are certain to lay your end of the finish line. That's really flaunting your tactical advantage!

GOLDEN RULES

- Avoid being blanketed.

- Avoid the hopeless position.

- Avoid being lee-bowed.

- Start near the favoured (upwind) end of the startline.

- Ignore the position of the windward mark when deciding where to start (providing the first leg is a beat).

- Keep in the front rank before the start.

- Take a transit so you know when you're on the line.

- Keep between your opponent and the next mark.

- Offwind, keep your wind clear and try to sail straight for the next mark.

Strategy

I n the absence of other boats there will often be a preferred way to go on the beat, reach or run. Quite often the strategic factors outweigh the tactical ones; for instance it may well be necessary to start at the downwind end of the line in order to sail into a favourable current.

SHORT BEATS

If the first beat is short, as is often the case when racing inland, it will be too risky to start at the port end of the line if there are a number of boats in the race. A short beat means that most of the fleet will arrive at the windward mark at the same time. It is far safer to approach this mark with right of way on starboard tack rather than risk coming in on port looking for a gap that may not exist. It is also advisable to overstand the mark slightly. You are likely to be approaching the mark on starboard behind other boats and the disturbed air will reduce your pointing ability alarmingly.

The most important strategic considerations are variation of wind strength and direction, and tidal current. Before the start of a race it is essential to take account of the prevailing conditions on the course and work out how they are going to affect you on the beat and, later, on the downwind legs.

CURRENT

It is an advantage to sail in the area where the current is strongest when it's with you and where the current is weakest when it's against you.

Where the port side of the first beat is favoured you can start wherever the tactical considerations dictate, then continue on starboard tack towards the left side of the course. If the starboard side of the course is best then you may have to start at or towards that end, in order to be able to tack after the start and go that way.

Determining the direction of the current

It isn't always easy to know which way the current is flowing. Here are a few pointers.

Before each race, find out the times of high and low water and write them on your boat with a chinagraph pencil.

Look at a chart or tidal atlas to see which way the tide will be going during the race. Draw a picture on your boat to remind you.

If you expect the tide to turn during the race, set the alarm on your watch to go off half an hour before. This will remind you to look out for the tidal change.

Once on the racecourse you need to see if the tidal predictions are correct. In fact tides are affected by barometric pressure and wind, so don't expect the published data to be precise.

- Look at moored boats. Since they are usually anchored at the bow, they swing with the tidal flow.

- Sail near a buoy whenever you get the chance and look to see if there is a swirl past it.

- If in doubt, drop a half-empty beer can near a fixed object (a buoy or a post) and see which way it drifts. Be sure to retrieve the can after use – you may need it again.

Determining when the tide turns

- Expect the tide to turn roughly when the published data predicts.

- Watch anchored boats to see when they swing.

- Wind-against-tide causes larger waves than wind-with-tide. So watching the sea state gives a tidal clue.

- Watch the flow past buoys.

Where is the current strongest?

Water is slowed down by friction (with the bottom or the shore). It also tends to flow in a straight line unless forced to bend. It follows that the strongest current is in deep water, such as the middle of a channel, and round the outside of bends. In bays there may even be back eddies.

Naturally you will try to sail in the weakest current when the flow is against you, and in the strongest current when the flow is with you. When sailing against the tide:

- Keep inshore.

- Keep in shallow water.

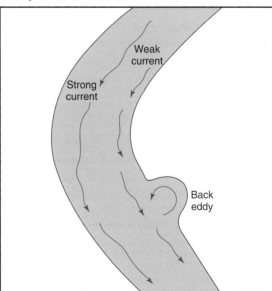

- Go for the inside of bends.

- Head for bays.

Do the opposite when the tide is with you.

GENERAL STRATEGY ON THE BEAT

In the absence of windshifts or current variations, tack within a 60-degree cone. Note that your tacks get more frequent as you approach the weather mark. Under no circumstances should you approach either layline, because if the wind shifts you will find yourself either overstanding or sailed across. In the diagram, boat A is on the layline, comfortably ahead of boat B. If the wind lifts A has overstood and B reaches the mark first. If the wind heads neither can lay the mark and both should tack. Once again, B comes out ahead.

WINDSHIFTS AND WINDBENDS

A windshift occurs when the direction of the wind suddenly alters.

A windbend is a gradual, permanent bending of the wind over a large area of water.

You need to take account of variations in wind direction, although they are not as predictable as current variations and therefore not as reliable. If wind and current demand different sides of the course, and the decision is finely balanced, go for the best current every time.

Compass sailing

The only reliable way to spot windshifts and bends is with a compass. Here's how to use it.

Before the start, beat on starboard tack. Keep the front of the jib just lifting all the time and watch the compass numbers moving behind the line on the case: '270, 275, 270, 265, 270, 270' you say to yourself. It's obvious that the wind is averaging 270, so write this by the compass. Now sail on, and watch to see if the bearing alters.

In a shifting wind you might expect readings like this: 270, 280, 280, 270, 260, 260, 260, 270.... The wind

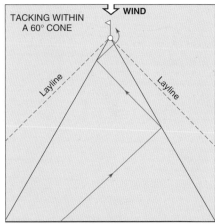

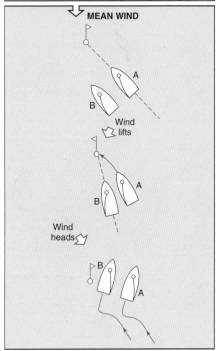

has swung right (veered) 10 degrees, then swung left (backed) 10 degrees. We will see later that you can tack on these shifts with advantage. For now try to find the period of the shifts – do they swing every minute, or every half-minute?

In a windbend you would expect the readings to alter gradually (and you'd expect the bend to be there on the next lap, too): '270, 275, 280, 285, 290, 295...'.

Having sorted the readings on starboard, tack and repeat the exercise on port. Write down the mean wind there too, and the limits of its wanderings. Then when you're actually racing you've got a lot of background wind information to go on.

Using windshifts

Short-term windshifts are caused by two principal effects:

1 As the wind flows around obstacles such as buildings and islands it becomes turbulent and inconsistent in direction.

2 The wind at higher altitudes always blows in a different direction from the wind at sea level. Under certain conditions chunks of this high air come down to sea level. The new air is not only moving faster but is going in a different direction from the prevailing wind, so you are hit by a shifting gust.

Some of the shifts are more pronounced and last longer than others – it is these that you have to spot and use.

In shifty winds, stay close to the middle of the beat. Tack each time the wind heads you (forces you to alter course *away* from the mark). In the diagram, boat C takes no account of windshifts. Note how little progress it makes to windward compared with boat D, which tacks each time the wind heads it.

The main problem is to differentiate between a real shift and a short-lived change in the wind. For that reason, sail on into each shift for five or ten seconds to make sure it's going to last. If a header lasts that long, tack.

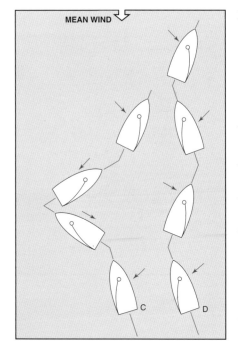

MEAN WIND

If you find yourself tacking too often, or are confused, sail on one tack for a while until you're sure what the wind is doing. Remember that you usually lose at least a boat's length each time you tack, so there always has to be a good reason to do so.

Using windbends

Permanent windbends are often caused by a land mass upwind of you. In the diagram the curved shoreline is causing the bend. Always sail towards the centre of a bend (like E in the diagram). In that way you are lifted on both tacks.

ONE-SIDED BEATS

If the course has been badly laid, or there has been a permanent windshift, the beat will be one-sided. (You will sail longer on one tack than the other.)

In this case always sail the long tack first. Then if the wind shifts even further, you may be able to lay the mark without tacking at all. If it stays steady you lose nothing. If it swings back towards the old direction, you are already on the favoured side of the course: tack, and sail across the opposition on the new lifted tack.

Watch the other boats

At the beginning of the first beat ask your crew to pick one boat of your standard that is going right and one that is going left. At the windward mark, check which came out ahead. This will give you a clue as to which side of the beat paid off.

Repeat on each beat. If you reckon the same side is paying every time, go that way. But if the evidence is inconclusive, stick to the 60-degree cone.

STRATEGY ON THE REACH

The shortest distance is a direct line between the two marks and many boat lengths can be lost by steering an erratic or curved course down the reach.

When you are sailing across a current it's useful to find a transit on the shore beyond the next mark (or otherwise one on the shore behind the previous mark) to

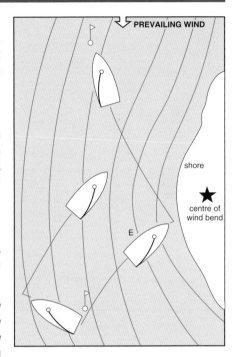

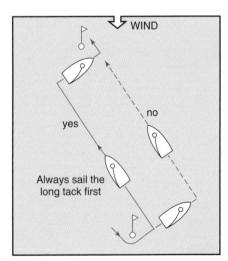

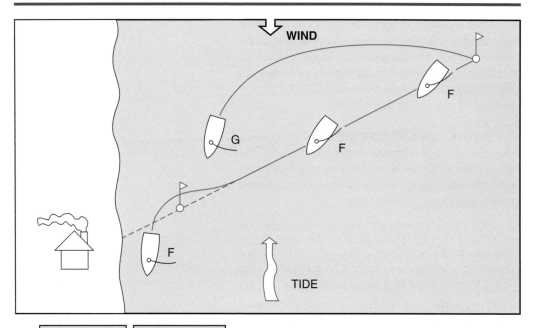

WIND

F

G

F

F

TIDE

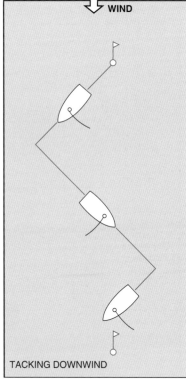

WIND

TACKING DOWNWIND

help you stay on the rhumb line. Simply pointing the bow at the mark will ensure that you sail a long curve as the current sweeps you off course. When the current is taking you upwind of the rhumb line you will, by steering low (like F in the diagram), gain enormously over the unwary (like G) who will end up running back towards the mark against the tide. They will slow dramatically; meanwhile you will storm through them on a reach, and round the buoy well ahead.

In general, luff as the wind drops, and bear away quickly as it increases. In this way you meet each gust sooner and stay with it longer. If you need to bear away, try to choose a header: you will then lose no speed and can luff again when the wind frees once more.

STRATEGY ON THE RUN

In many boats – particularly those with spinnakers (and of course all catamarans) – the fastest course on a running leg will not be the rhumb line but one that takes advantage of the extra speed of a broad reach. So long as the speed gain more than offsets the extra distance you need to travel, then gybing downwind will pay.

Because it is a mirror image of the beat, this process is often called (perhaps rather confusingly) tacking downwind. The trick is to know how much to aim up from the rhumb line. In general, the lighter the wind the more you should head up. On average you will find that your best course is 10 degrees off the dead run.

Gybing on shifts and on the tide

If the run is not true, choose the gybe that heads nearest the mark. (This is similar to choosing the long tack first, when beating.) Then if the wind heads, you simply speed up. If it frees, you can gybe.

As on the beat, windshifts can be used with advantage on the run. The idea is to keep at a constant angle to the wind. As it heads you bear away – that's great, you're now pointing more directly towards the mark. If it lifts you will need to sail further off the rhumb line to keep up speed, and should gybe so as to sail more directly down the rhumb line. Note in the diagram how H gybes on each shift and sails fast straight to the leeward mark.

If you think the wind is going to shift a short way down the run (your experience on the beat will give this away) then initially choose the direction that will allow you to gybe when the wind shifts (and then point directly at the mark on a broad reach).

If there is an uneven current or tide across the course, choose to cross the strongest tide on the gybe that gives the most advantage. J crosses the strong tide on port; the tide pushes her sail through the air, and 'squirts' her forward. K does the opposite, and her sail backs in the strong tidal region.

STRATEGY AT THE FINISH

Many places can be lost by finishing at the wrong end of the line if it is significantly biased. Remember, it will be quicker to reach the downwind end – the opposite end to the one you would aim to start from! The best way to judge this at the end of the last beat is by sailing on a layline towards one end. Let's say you're on port tack just laying the starboard end of the line. As

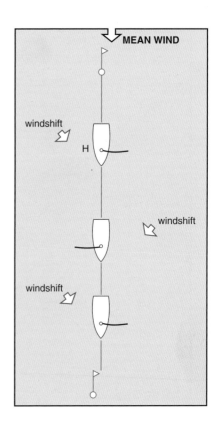

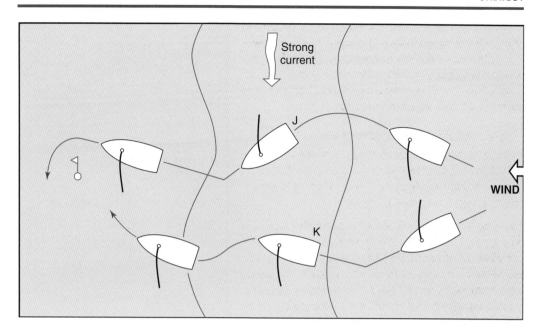

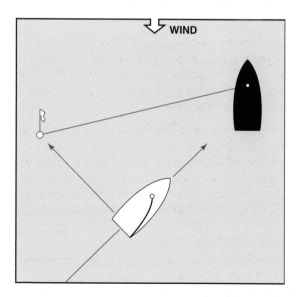

you cross the other layline you can judge which is the shorter distance to the finish. In the diagram the pin end is favoured, so tack and finish by the buoy.

If the line was already set on the previous round and the wind direction is relatively steady you can assess the situation on the penultimate lap and make your plans in advance.

GOLDEN RULES

- On a short beat keep to the right-hand side of the course.

- Find out which way the current or tide is flowing.

- Head for deep water and the outside of bends when the tide is with you.

- If everything is equal, tack up a 60-degree cone.

- STAY WELL INSIDE THE LAY-LINES.

- Use your compass to spot windshifts.

- Tack on headers.

- Sail towards the centre of wind-bends.

- On a one-sided beat, sail the long leg first.

- When sailing cross-tide, point into the tide and use a transit to sail a straight course 'over the land'.

- Gybe on windshifts.

- Choose the gybe that takes you most directly to the lee-ward mark.

- Keep strong tide under your lee bow.

- Go for the downwind end of the finish line.

Tuning

Some boats are faster than others, even when they are one-designs. This difference is often called boatspeed. Boatspeed is great when you've got it: as someone once said, 'Boatspeed makes you a tactical genius'.

A friend who is a racing driver was amazed at the effort we put in to speed up from, say, 6 knots to 6.1 knots. He was more interested in getting up to 200 mph! Yet if you were going 0.1 knots faster you'd be 300 metres further up the fleet by the finish; this difference might well be magnified still further, because the leading boats slow up those behind.

So why do good crews have better boatspeed? The answer is that they can recognise a slow boat and do something about it. The beginner is never sure whether it's the boat or his technique that's wrong. But do bear in mind that you can almost always improve your technique more than you can improve the boat. It's only when you're looking for the last fraction of a percent that you need to start spending money.

GENERAL REQUIREMENTS

Let's suppose that you're relatively happy with your technique and are on the boatspeed trail. The first thing to do is…enjoy it! Tuning is largely trial and error, yet more rubbish is talked about it than any other aspect of sailing. There is no point in slavishly following some set formula; you're more likely to get good speed by having fun playing around with different settings.

Having said that, there's no point in trying to tune a badly-prepared boat (see Chapter 6). Your sails must be in good condition too: one season's use is maximum if you want to win a national championship, two seasons for a club series. It's a sad fact of life that cloth does deteriorate with use, and flapping causes the finish to break down.

Finally, it is impossible to tune a boat unless you're sailing her *upright*. Any discernable heel will affect the balance; all dinghies are designed to be sailed upright.

WHAT ARE WE TRYING TO DO?

All boats are tuned for the beat. (Having got them right for upwind work, all you have to do offwind is to make the sails fuller, and perhaps rake the mast forward.)

The main objective is to be able to adjust the curve (belly) in the sails for the wind strength. You want maximum fullness (which gives maximum power) in medium winds. As the breeze builds, you need to gradually flatten the sails to reduce their power – otherwise you'll be unable to hold the boat up. Surprisingly, you need quite flat sails in light airs too, because the feeble breeze is incapable of bending around highly-curved sails.

The mainsail is cut with a curved luff. When this is set on a straight mast, fullness is forced into the sail. To remove the fullness, simply bend the mast: when the curve in the mast matches the curve in the luff, the sail will be almost flat. (Not quite flat, because some curve is also built into the sail by curving the edges of the panels.) The chief aim here is to match the mast bend to the luff curve – if the mast over-bends at any point, horrible creases form from that point.

The jib is not set on a mast, but the front edge is controlled in a similar way via rig tension. Sloppy rigging puts curve into the front of the jib, whereas tight rigging pulls the jib luff straight and gets rid of fullness. In

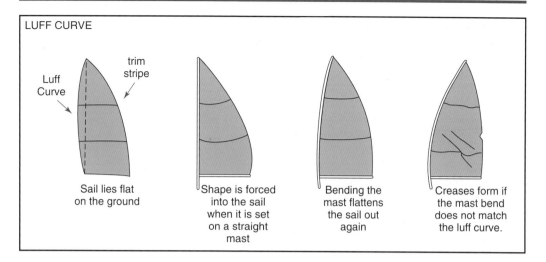

LUFF CURVE

Luff Curve

trim stripe

Sail lies flat on the ground

Shape is forced into the sail when it is set on a straight mast

Bending the mast flattens the sail out again

Creases form if the mast bend does not match the luff curve.

general, about 160 kg (350 lbs) tension on the jib luff wire is a good starting point.

One more objective is to balance the helm. With the boat beating in a medium breeze, and upright, there should be a very slight pull on the tiller. (This is weather helm.) Too much weather helm is bad because the rudder is then going through the water at an angle, which slows the boat down. But lee helm is disastrous, because the flow of water over the rudder forces the boat to leeward. Never rig a boat for lee helm.

WHAT DO ALL THE CONTROLS DO?

Shrouds
The shrouds control mast rake. If you shorten the shrouds, you rake the mast aft; if you make them longer, you reduce the aft rake.

Jib halyard
The jib halyard pulls the mast up tight against the pull of the shrouds; in other words tightening the jib halyard increases tension. The primary aim here is to stop the luff of the jib sagging, as this forces fullness into the front of the sail and stops you pointing. A secondary effect of rig tension is that it allows the spreaders to control mast bend.

Jib fairlead

The position of the jib fairlead controls the slot (the gap between the jib and the mainsail). If the slot is narrow, the rig is powered up; if it's wide, the rig is depowered. There are three ways of moving the fairlead – fore-and-aft, up-and-down- and side-to-side. Moving the fairlead *forward*, *down* and *in* all close the slot and increase power.

Jib sheet

The tension on the job sheet is critical. A tight sheet gives a flat sail with a hard leech, whereas a loose sheet gives the opposite. The difference between tight and loose is only about five centimetres (two inches), so it's best to mark the sheet at its optimum position. You can find this by sighting the sail from behind, and adjusting the fairlead and sheet until the leech of the jib is parallel to the closest part of the main.

The jib sheet tension is too tight (left), too loose (centre) and correct (right).

Spreaders

The spreaders control the bend in the middle of the mast. Raking the spreaders aft bows the middle of the mast forwards; raking the spreaders forward straightens the mast again. Lengthening the spreaders stiffens the mast sideways; shortening the spreaders lets the middle of the mast bow to windward, which is a (rather dubious) way of depowering the rig.

The rake of the spreaders is usually measured as the distance from the back of the mast to a straight line across the spreader tips (see photo Chapter 6 page 36).

Mast ram

Mast rams are only fitted on boats where the mast passes through the deck and is stepped on the hog. The ram controls mast bend low down. If you release the ram (or remove chocks) the mast automatically bows forwards, whereas tensioning the ram (or adding chocks) pushes the mast aft and stiffens it.

Kicking strap (vang)

The kicker (vang) pulls both down *and* forwards. The downwards pull helps prevent the leech of the main twisting, provided the boom is stiff (otherwise the boom bends and the effect is lost). The forwards pull presses the boom against the mast, which bends forwards (unless the ram is tensioned).

The vang is too tight (left and centre) and too loose (right).

Mainsheet

The mainsheet allows the boom to swing in and out. But once the boom is on the centreline, increasing mainsheet tension pulls down on the boom, which in turn tightens the leech. This is a similar effect to that of the kicking strap (vang), but if the sheet take-off points on the boom are vertically above the traveller you can tighten the leech of the main without bending the mast.

The mainsheet is too tight (left). Easing the mainsheet reduces tension and opens the leech (right).

Cunningham

The Cunningham tensions the luff of the main, which pulls the fullness forward, ruining your pointing ability in light and medium winds. It also removes the creases near the luff. The Cunningham also slackens the leech of the main, so in practice it is only used when you're

Increased Cunningham tension in the right hand picture removes creases in the luff and reduces leech tension.

Loosening the outhaul increases the depth in the foot of the sail and tightens the lower leech.

overpowered. Ignore those creases: they don't really slow you down much.

Outhaul

The outhaul stretches the foot of the main. Tensioning it reduces the draft in the foot of the sail and stops the leech just above the boom curling to windward. Both effects are admirable when beating, so always have the outhaul tight to windward. Let it off on the reach and the run to give a baggy sail.

INITIAL SET-UP ONSHORE

You need first to get the mast in roughly the right position. You can do this on land, with the mainsail *down*.

Hoist the jib and pull the halyard really tight. If you have a tension meter, test the jib luff tension: it should be about 114 kg (250 lb). If you don't have a meter, it should give a satisfying twang when plucked.

Sight up the mast. There should be no sideways bend. Take the end of the halyard to each chainplate to check the mast isn't leaning to one side.

Sight up the mast again, while pulling the main halyard tight between the top of the mast and the gooseneck. There should be a reasonable, progressive bend: a maximum of 5–10 centimetres (2–4 inches) is a sensible place to start.

The rake of the mast is measured by fixing a tape measure to the main halyard, running it up to the top of the mast, and measuring to the centre of the top of the transom. Try to get an expert to give you his rake figures, then copy them. For example, on a 470 the rake should be 6.76 metres (22 feet, 2 inches) for light winds, progressing to 6.65 metres (21 feet, 10 inches) for strong winds.

Failing this, put the boat on the water and hang a heavy weight (such as a toolbox) from the main halyard. Measure the distance from the halyard to the back of the mast at gooseneck level: about 20 centimetres (8 inches) is a good starting point.

INITIAL SET-UP ON WATER

Now for the fun bit!

Choose a day with a medium wind and fairly flat water, rig the boat and get her sailing properly on a beat. Remember to keep the hull flat throughout this exercise.

Pull in the mainsheet almost as hard as you can with one hand. Your mainsail should set nicely. If there are horrible creases coming out of the centre of the mast, reduce the mast bend by tensioning the ram and/or raking the spreaders forwards. But if you can't get creases by pulling really hard on the mainsheet, increase the mast bend.

Now let go of the tiller. If the boat is flat, she should luff very slowly. If she luffs hard, you have weather helm and need to rake the mast forward, move it forward bodily (with the same rake), loosen the leech of the main by bending the mast, rake the centreboard aft or move the centreboard pivot aft.

If the boat bears away when you let go of the tiller, you have lee helm. This is disastrous, so rake the mast back, move it aft at the foot, tighten the leech by straightening the mast, rake the centreboard forward or move the centreboard pivot forward.

ADJUSTING THE RIG FOR VARIOUS WINDSTRENGTHS

Each class is different, but here are a few general pointers to tweaking for various windstrengths.

- As the wind builds, the kicking strap (vang) should be pulled tighter.

- When the wind is light, let off the ram to bend the mast. In medium winds the mast needs to be fairly straight for maximum power. As you become overpowered, gradually bend the mast more by letting off the ram once again to flatten the sail.

GOLDEN RULES

- You can always improve your technique more than you can improve your boat.

- Tune your boat for the beat.

- Mast bend controls sail shape.

- The shrouds control rake.

- The jib halyard controls rig tension.

- Raking the spreaders aft bends the mast.

- Use the Cunningham only when overpowered.

- Tension the outhaul when beating.

- In light winds ease the mainsheet slightly, with the vang slack. In medium winds pull it tight. In strong winds ease the mainsheet again (with tight vang).

- The mast should be gradually raked back as the wind increases. This reduces the overlap between jib and main, thereby depowering the rig. This does not increase weather helm, because the mainsheet will be eased in these conditions.

- In strong winds raise the centreboard or daggerboard a little. When a gust hits, the boat slides sideways instead of tripping over the centreboard and heeling excessively.

The adjustments to make as you go 'through the gears' are summed up in the following table.

	Mainsheet	Vang	Cunningham	Outhaul	Rig Tension	Jib fairlead
Light	Eased	Eased	Eased	Tight	Tight	Down (or forward)
Medium	Tight	Medium	Eased	Eased two inches	Tight	Down (or forward)
Strong	Eased	Very tight	Tight	Tight	Tighter or eased depending on class	Up (or aft)

The Spinnaker

The spinnaker adds great interest to downwind sailing, particularly for your crew. It adds excitement and tactical interest to the run, gives power on the reach and puts a premium on good gybing technique.

SPINNAKER GEAR

In a dinghy, the spinnaker is usually set from just above the jib, and the sheets are led outside all the sails to blocks well aft in the boat. A spinnaker pole is attached to the weather corner (the tack), which helps to stabilise the spinnaker and, on the run, increases the width exposed to the wind. The pole setting also affects the general shape of the sail.

The line from the pole corner is called the guy, whereas the other line is the sheet. A twinning line or hook is used to pull down the guy, keeping it out of the crew's way and keeping the pull of the guy at the correct angle. An uphaul and downhaul control the vertical angle of the pole.

It's more important that all the spinnaker gear works one hundred percent than any of the other equipment because a problem in raising or lowering can lose you a huge distance. Ensure that the pole end fittings work

Uphaul
Pole
Downhaul
Guy
Sheet

effectively and will only release the sheet or guy when required.

The pole and controls

The pole uphaul and downhaul systems should be positive, only relying on elastic to retract the arrangement when the pole is taken down. If your class rules allow it, the pole should be stowed along the boom, from where it can be quickly and easily set by the crew.

The sheet and guy

Use non-stretch rope for the sheet and guy. The leads should be as far aft and as far outboard as possible to open the leech of the kite and reduce backwinding of the mainsail.

The halyard

Quick setting of the spinnaker can be achieved when you haven't a chute by fitting a pump system. This is a multi-purchase halyard that works in reverse: as you pull upwards the halyard moves double or triple the distance you pull. Two pumps should be enough to raise the kite completely.

RAISING AND LOWERING THE SPINNAKER

A great deal of time, and consequently speed, can be lost during setting and lowering of the spinnaker. In particular, setting the kite at the beginning of a close reach can cost you a lot of time. The sail must go up as quickly as possible for two reasons: a flapping spinnaker creates enormous drag on the reach (as opposed to the run where this drag is actually in the right direction), and it's very likely to get twisted during a slow hoist.

The kite is best launched from the leeward side in the lee of mainsail and jib, which means that you need to take this into account when preparing it before the start or when taking it down. Generally this means stowing it on the port side if the weather mark is to port or the starboard side if the first mark is to starboard. The photo sequences show how to launch the kite both from the leeward and the windward side. Note that you always pull the kite down on the windward side.

The spinnaker chute

If your boat has a spinnaker chute then many of these problems are solved.

Advantages

So long as the chute is of large diameter the spinnaker will go up quite fast. The helmsman can pull it up while the crew sheets it in, so it will rarely get twisted. It is also very easily doused: as the crew attends to the spinnaker pole the helmsman simply releases the continuous halyard and pulls rapidly on the downhaul line. However, if the halyard is allowed to run before the downhaul is pulled in the spinnaker can end up under the bow of the boat, which spells real disaster!

A fast spinnaker hoist from the leeward bag.

If the kite is in the windward bag you will need to do a chuck hoist.

Disadvantages
The spinnaker chute itself adds weight to the front of the boat, and even more weight if the water is trapped inside the spinnaker. A flap over the mouth of the chute will deflect water to some degree.

RUNNING

When running, the pole should be pulled right aft to expose the maximum area of the sail to the wind. The tack and clew (the two bottom corners) should be set at approximately the same height by adjusting the pole height. The sheet is then eased until the weather edge (the luff) is just about to collapse.

REACHING

As the apparent wind moves forward let the pole go forward and pull in the sheet. At this point it may pay to raise the pole a few inches.

Here the pole is too high letting air escape from the top of the spinnaker.

Pull the guy back on the run to present more sail area to the wind. If the pole is too far forward (right) the spinnaker is blanketed by the main.

Many inexperienced crews sail slowly on spinnaker reaches with their poles too low. This makes the spinnaker too full at the front. Raising the pole flattens the leading edge, allowing better pointing for a given setting. Overtrimming the sheet will badly backwind the mainsail. Keep easing the sheet until the luff is on the point of falling in.

Close reaching

A good reaching spinnaker can be used effectively even if the apparent wind is ahead of abeam. Skill and experience helps greatly on this point of sailing.

The pole needs to be well forward but, if possible, not quite against the jib luff. The guy needs to be cleated close to the weather shroud since even a small degree of stretch affects the pole angle greatly. In order to sheet the spinnaker sufficiently to keep it pulling, some backwinding of the mainsail is inevitable. To minimise this, ease the kicking strap (vang) and trim the mainsheet towards the centreline. Raising the boom in this way also reduces its chances of hitting the water should you heel excessively, frees the spinnaker sheet (which raises the clew of the kite slightly), and reduces the heeling moment of the mainsail by opening the top of the sail. You will need to hike harder to offset the extra side forces. Raise your board to about halfway to help reduce heeling.

There are two good reasons why you may decide *not* to carry your spinnaker on the close reach:

1 Because the reach is just too close to the wind for it to pay off. That is, the extra forward drive may be so slight that the very act of putting up and taking down the sail will lose you more than you will gain. In general, if the halyard points abeam or aft of abeam, the spinnaker is not paying and should be taken down.

2 Because the wind is too strong, and the boat will heel too much, spilling wind and making it difficult to hold a course above or on the line to the next mark.

In the first case you must rely on experience or watch the other boats to determine the best course of action. In the second case, again watch the rest of the fleet. As a beginner the best advice is: if in doubt don't use your spinnaker on a close reach if it's windy. However, as

Gybing the spinnaker. Once the boom has gone across, the helmsman steers with his legs while holding the sheet and guy, to keep the kite full throughout the manoeuvre.

On a reach, ease the sheet to keep the spinnaker leech away from the main (right).

To lower the spinnaker, take off the pole and stow it, then pull the sail down into the windward bag while the helmsman progressively releases the halyard.

you gain experience a good general rule is: if you are not sitting out hard *without* it up (or, on a trapeze boat, the crew is not on the wire) then you will probably be able to hold the spinnaker with the increased leverage available.

GYBING THE SPINNAKER

The spinnaker adds a little more interest to gybing. When you are proficient you should be able to complete the gybe without the spinnaker collapsing, but this takes practice!

Here's the procedure. Pull the leeward twinning line in tight and release the weather one. Bear away, rolling the boat to weather. Just before the boom comes over the crew should pull the pole back so that the spinnaker swings round and sets on the new leeward side.

He should then remove the pole end from the mast and clip it to the new guy before disconnecting the other end (from the new sheet) and attaching it to the mast. After the gybe the helmsman can hold the sheet and guy while standing astride the tiller. In this way the boat can be steered straight and the spinnaker kept full. Finally the crew takes over the sheet and guy, and the boat is away on the new gybe.

Practice is essential, particularly when gybing from a reach to a reach, which is more difficult because the helmsman is unable to hold the sheets. Always remember to gybe the boat when *you* want to, and don't let the boat decide the moment for you.

GOLDEN RULES

- Always put up the kite before the start to check it.

- Only fly a spinnaker if the halyard is pointing forward of abeam (and if you can keep the boat upright).

- Try to stow the spinnaker so it is launched from the leeward side.

- Always take the spinnaker down to windward.

- Always ease the sheet as much as possible.

- Adjust the pole height so the tack and clew of the spinnaker are equal heights above the water.

- Raise the pole on a close reach.

The Asymmetric Spinnaker

The alternative to the conventional (symmetrical) spinnaker is the asymmetric spinnaker, sometimes referred to as a gennaker because it is a halfway house between a genoa (large overlapping jib) and a spinnaker. As implied by the name, the shape is asymmetrical with a longer luff and a shorter leech. The tack is always attached on the centreline of the boat, usually to an extending pole.

The asymmetric spinnaker has advantages and disadvantages over the conventional spinnaker.

ADVANTAGES

As there is no conventional spinnaker pole, gybing is very much easier as the clew of the sail is simply pulled around the luff of the jib and sheeted on the opposite side.

In addition, because the asymmetric spinnaker is flatter, it acts as a large powerful jib and enables great speed to be achieved on a reach.

DISADVANTAGES

Because the tack is on the centreline of the boat, a large proportion of the sail will be blanketed by the mainsail as the boat tries to run before the wind. As a result, boats flying an asymmetric have to sail towards

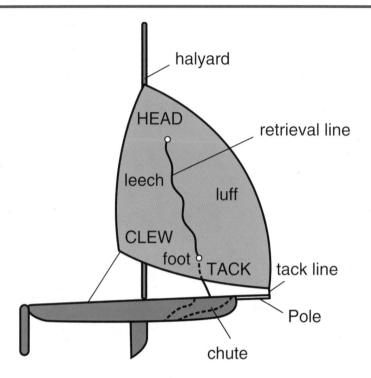

halyard

HEAD

retrieval line

leech

luff

CLEW

foot

TACK

tack line

Pole

chute

the leeward mark in a series of broad reaches in much the same way as a boat tacks towards the windward mark.

Nevertheless, the increase in speed more than makes up for the extra distance travelled in most reasonable wind strengths.

An asymmetric spinnaker is invariably launched from a spinnaker chute and retrieved back into the chute via a retrieval line, which is also in fact the spinnaker halyard. However, it's all too easy to rig the various lines – sheets, halyard, tack line and retrieval line – incorrectly, so time must be given to rigging the sail correctly before going afloat. Most asymmetrics have their three corners marked T, H, and C, for Tack, Head and Clew. If they are not marked, be sure to mark them yourself with an indelible marker pen.

Asymmetrics tack downwind.

Spinnaker launch on a close reach.

RIGGING YOUR ASYMMETRIC

To start, always lay out the spinnaker that you are rigging on the same side of the boat. In this way you will always be feeding the retrieval line the same way. For example, if the patches are on the front of the spinnaker, feed the retrieval line under the foot first.

Be sure to tie loose bowlines to the corners to avoid twist.

Begin by finding the *tack* and attaching this to the tack line with a bowline. Be sure that each bowline has a large enough loop to allow it to move around the cringle. Too tight a loop can lead to the corner of the sail setting with a local twist.

Now work along the luff of the spinnaker (usually a coloured tabling) until you reach the head. Tie the halyard once again using a loose looped bowline. Now follow the leech down to the clew to ensure that the sail is not twisted. It's a good idea not to attach the sheets at this stage but to work forward along the foot and go to work on threading the retrieval line

Lay out the asymmetric and attach the tack.

When this is in place attach the two sheets. Now turn the boat into the wind and pull up the sail on land (so long as it's not too windy) to check that you have got it right!

EQUIPMENT

With the high sheet load, it's normal to fit some form of ratchet block to assist in holding the sheet for any period of time in a blow. Unlike jib sheets that can be cleated, this is normally regarded as inadvisable on the spinnaker. Although a switchable ratchet block is often used, we are great believers in one of the widely

Attach the sheets.

Thread the retrieval line.

Before going afloat, pull up the asymmetric to check that it is correctly rigged.

available automatic ratchet blocks. This is because during the course of a gybe the trailing sheet (the one just released) needs to pay off with the minimum amount of drag.

Make sure you have an effective jam cleat for your halyard. There is nothing more embarrassing than to see the sail disappear in front of you when the halyard suddenly uncleats itself!

SETTING

Pulling up the sail is easy. Normally the helm pulls the spinnaker up while the crew pulls out the pole. On some arrangements pulling on the halyard also sets the pole (although this is slightly slower). As soon as the head is fully up the crew can sheet in and you are away. Beware of overtrimming and backwinding the mainsail. Keep easing the sheet until the luff is on the verge of breaking. This gives you the best speed.

Most important is to choose the correct angles to tack downwind. Clearly, if you travel closer to the wind the speed will be considerably greater but you will travel a greater distance. Conversely, sailing deep could mean a lot less distance to cover but at a much slower speed. Finding the optimum angle is therefore essential. This angle varies depending on the wind speed and also to a degree on the wave conditions. In light wind it generally pays to sail deep whereas in stronger winds luffing up until the boat is planing will increase boat speed sufficiently for the extra distance sailed to more than pay off. In short waves it nearly always pays to sail higher and faster, punching through the waves, than to sail deep. Some boats will need to be sailed higher than others. It's all largely a question of trial and error and essential that when you do get it right – that is, you find you are overtaking boats downwind – you make a mental note of the angles that you sailed. In trapeze boats, a good general rule is that if you are trapezing upwind then you will gain by trapezing downwind too.

Our advice is that once you have determined the ideal speed and angle to sail, you should position the crew appropriately and steer the boat to maintain the boat's

Ease the sheet until the luff is just on the point of breaking.

LIGHT WEATHER spinnaker hoist from the chute is very straightforward. Retrieval is equally straightforward.

A small degree of heel on a reach is permissible to balance the rudder.

heel for that particular righting moment. In other words having set yourself up to trapeze or otherwise, steer the boat higher on the wind if the boat starts to fall on top of you and bear off as the boat starts to heel away from you. Once you are confident in your chosen angle you will be able to sail without thinking and free up your mind for tactical decisions, such as which side of the run to sail and how far from the layline to gybe.

Trapezing with an asymmetric is the one occasion when a slight degree of heel is permissible. This is because the boat flying an asymmetric carries a degree of lee helm (has a tendency to bear away). A small amount of heel applies a countering weather helm and neutralises the steering.

In light winds one needs to sail as low as possible while still keeping the spinnaker full. To assist in this aim, and to project the luff as far to windward as possible,

In light winds, sit inboard and sail as deep as possible. Easing the halyard helps the asymmetric project to weather.

it helps to ease the halyard by an arm's length. When close reaching it is essential that the head is pulled right to the mast.

Dropping the asymmetric is a simple matter of uncleating the halyard/retrieval line and pulling the sail into the chute

GYBING

Gybing an asymmetric is easy.

Start the gybe by bearing away *quickly*. The boat will roll to windward. As it does so and you pass the dead downwind angle the helm pulls the boom across quickly. At the same time the crew should pull on the opposite sheet of the asymmetric quickly pulling it around the front of the jib and sheeting it on the new leeward side. The faster you can gybe the less the wind pressure is in the sails and the less heeling moment is encountered.

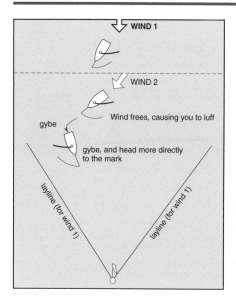

TACTICS

As with beating, there are laylines beyond which you should not sail. To do so will mean that you are sailing an unnecessary extra distance. Unless other factors dictate, always start the run on the gybe that will take you nearest to the direction of the leeward mark. If the wind frees as you progress down the run and causes you to have to luff up, this may well be the time to gybe in order to sail a shorter distance to the mark.

RULES

The one rule that newcomers to asymmetric sailing tend to forget is that of overlaps coming into a mark. In the diagram, boat A has an overlap on boat B and so long as they eventually converge inside the two boat circle A has the rights to water over B; indeed an

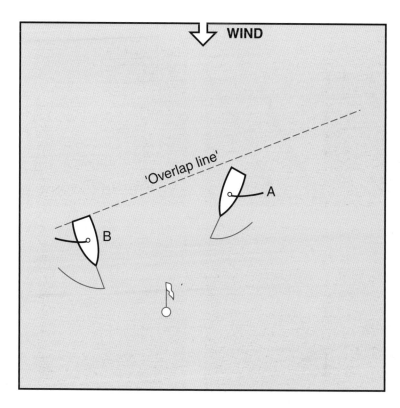

overlap has been occurring for a very long time. Remember an overlap at a leeward mark takes priority over port and starboard!

GOLDEN RULES

- Always launch the asymmetric on land before sailing, if possible, to ensure it is correctly rigged.

- If your crew has trapezed on the beat it usually pays to trapeze the 'runs' too.

- Sail as low as possible in light winds and project the kite to windward.

- Ease the halyard or tack-line when sailing low.

- Don't sail beyond the lay-lines on the 'run'.

- Beware the over-lap rule when approaching the leeward mark.

Glossary

Bearing away Altering course away from the wind

Blanketing Positioning yourself between your opponent and the wind, to reduce the wind available to him.

Camber The curve or belly in a sail.

Committee boat The boat which controls the race, usually moored at one end of the startline.

Covering Staying between your opponent and the next mark.

Deep Sailing 'deep' means sailing as low a course as possible on a run.

Dirty wind The turbulent wind to leeward of a sail and in line with it.

Feathering A temporary and subtle luff, on a beat, to depower the sails.

Foils The rudder blade and centreboard.

Free (also called Footing) Sailing a little off the wind on a beat, with sheets eased, to improve speed at the expense of pointing ability.

Gate start A method of starting a one-design fleet where a port tack boat beats across the fleet, the other boats passing under her stern.

Handicap race A method of racing boats of different classes together, using a handicap to correct for their different speeds.

Header A windshift, so the wind comes more from the bow.

In irons Stopped head to wind, unintentionally.

Inner distance mark (IDM) A buoy laid approximately on the startline near the committee boat. Competitors may not pass between the two.

Layline Imaginary lines depicting the port and starboard close-hauled courses to the windward mark. Also applicable downwind.

Lee-bow effect When one boat, slightly ahead and to leeward, deflects wind onto the lee side of a pursuing boat's sails.

Lee helm A boat has lee helm it it bears away if the tiller is released when beating.

Leeward boat A boat downwind of another.

Leeward mark The mark rounded at the beginning of the beat. The most downwind mark of the course (except for starting marks).

Lift A wind shift that allows one to point higher (opposite to 'header').

Luff Altering course towards the wind.

Mast rake How far aft the mast leans.

Officer of the day (OOD) The person in charge of racing on a particular day.

Outer Distance Mark (ODM) The buoy that limits the length of the start line (usally at the port end).

Overlap An overlap exists when the bow of a pursuing boat is ahead of an imaginary line through the aftmost point of the leading boat, and at right angles to that boat.

Pinch Beat too close to the wind.

Pointing A boat sailing very close to the wind is said to be pointing well, although she may be a little slower through the water than a boat sailing free.

Protest A protest is lodged by shouting "protest" at the time of the incident. The protest meeting is similar to a court of law.

Pursuit race Boats start at times determined by their handicap, and the first across the line is the winner.

Rhumb line The direct line to the next mark.

Roll tack A light weather tack in which the boat is rolled, thus fanning the sails through the air.

Safe leeward position The leading yacht establishes herself in front and to leeward of her opponent (see lee-bow effect).

Sailing instructions Written instructions on the management of a race, and the course to be sailed.

Starboard! If two yachts are on opposite tacks (have different windward sides) the one on starboard tack has right of way.

Tacking downwind Sailing downwind in a series of broad reaches, connected by gybes, to try and reach the leeward mark faster.

Transit Two fixed objects aligned to give an imaginary line or bearing.

Two-Turns Penalty If the sailing instructions allow it doing two turns including two tacks and two gybes can exonerate a boat after certain infringements.

Up, up, up! The leeward boat is requesting the windward boat to luff.

Water! A request for room to round a mark or obstruction, or to tack clear of an object.

Weather helm A boat that luffs when the tiller is let go has weather helm.

Weather mark The most windward mark of the course, excepting finishing marks.

Wetted area The surface of the hull that is immersed.

Wind backs When the wind shifts anticlockwise.

Windbend A progressive windshift, i.e. one that becomes more pronounced as you travel into it.

Wind shadow The area to leeward of a sail where the wind is lessened.

Windshift A change in the direction of the wind.

Wind veers When the wind shifts clockwise.

Windward boat The boat that is nearer the wind.

RACE SIGNALS

The meanings of visual and sound signals are stated below. An arrow pointing up or down (▲▼) means that a visual signal is displayed or removed. A dot (•) means a sound; dots with dashes (• - - - •) mean repetitive sounds. When a visual signal is displayed over a class flag, the signal applies only to that class.

Postponement Signals

▲ • • ▼ •

AP Races not started are *postponed*. The warning signal will be made 1 minute after removal unless at that time the race is postponed again or *abandoned*.

▲ • •

AP over H Races not started are *postponed*. Further Signals ashore.

▲ • •

AP over A Races not started are *postponed*. No more racing today.

Penant 1 ▲ • • ▼ •

Penant 2 ▲ • • ▼ •

Penant 3 ▲ • • ▼ •

Penant 4 ▲ • • ▼ •

Penant 5 ▲ • • ▼ •   **Penant 6** ▲ • • ▼ •

A-P over a numeral pennant 1-6 *Postponement* of 1-6 hours from the scheduled starting time

Abandonment Signals

▲ • • • ▼ •

N All races that have started are *abandoned*. Return to the starting area. The warning signal will be made 1 minute after removel unless at that time the race is *abandoned* again or *postponed*.

▲ • • •

N over H All races are *abandoned*. Further signals ashore.

▲ • • •

N over A All races are *abandoned*. No more racing today.

Recall Signals

▲ •

X Individual recall

• - - - •

First Substitute General recall. The warning signal will be made 1 minute after removal.

Signals before the Start

▲ • ▼ •

P Preparatory signal.

▲ • ▼ •

I Rule 30.1 is in effect.

▲ • ▼ •

Z Rule 30.2 is in effect.

▲ • ▼ •

Black flag. Rule 30.3 is in effect.

Course Change

▲ • •

S The course has been shortened. Rule 32.2 is in effect.

• - - - •

C The position of the next *mark* has been changed.

Other Signals

▲ •

L Ashore: A notice to competitors has been posted. Afloat: Come within hail or follow this boat.

• - - - •

M The object displaying this signal replaces a missing *mark*.

▲ •

Y Wear personal buoyancy.

(no sound)

Blue flag or shape. This race committee boat is in position at the finishing line.

You rely on us.
Can we rely on you?

Become an Offshore member
from just £5 a month.

Last year , our volunteers rescued over 8,000 people but we couldn't have rescued a single one of them without the support of people like you. Join Offshore today, and you'll be helping to run the lifeboat service, whose volunteers will be on hand, should you ever get into difficulty at sea

Please call **0800 543210** quoting 'FB07'
or visit **rnli.org.uk**

Offshore